Selected Topics in Modern Biology

The Origin of Life

SECOND EDITION

JOHN KEOSIAN

Professor of Biology
Newark College of Arts and Sciences
Rutgers ● The State University
and Experimental Biologist
The Newark Beth Israel Hospital

 VAN NOSTRAND REINHOLD COMPANY

New York Cincinnati Toronto London Melbourne

TO JULIE

577
K430
85196
oct 1973

Van Nostrand Reinhold Company Regional Offices:
New York   Cincinnati   Chicago   Millbrae   Dallas

Van Nostrand Reinhold Company International Offices:
London   Toronto   Melbourne

Published by Van Nostrand Reinhold Company
450 West 33rd Street, New York, N.Y. 10001

10 9 8 7 6 5 4 3 2

Preface

Interest in the chemical origin of life continues unabated. Oparin's contribution ("The Origin of Life," 1936) must go down in history as having stimulated the modern phase of experimentation on the problem of life's origin. The belief which formerly paralyzed all thinking on the origin of life, namely that only living things can synthesize organic compounds, is now completely shattered. But as that barrier was demolished, problems which appeared minor in the face of that impasse now urgently come to the fore, and the present era of experimentation has raised its own crop of questions. As the evidence from all quarters accumulates, modifications in the original hypothesis seem necessary. The direction that these modifications will take is not yet clear. Controversies are becoming more numerous and sharper. Strictly speaking, the only generally accepted point in the whole problem is the premise that the abiotic formation of organic compounds preceded the origin of life.

The present edition is given in two parts. Part I presents briefly the less controversial aspects of the problem. Much of the rapidly growing list of organic compounds which have been synthesized under simulated primitive earth conditions is given in condensed form in Table 4-2. This table can be treated as a reference and is not essential to the continuity of the text. The material in Part II (Chapters six to ten) considers some of the broader questions and controversies of the problem of the origin of life, thus, hopefully, furnishing a better perspective on the proliferating literature.

In the limited space of this book it was not possible to cite all the sources that were consulted, or to discuss all the aspects of the problem that have arisen, but an attempt was made to present a balanced spectrum. The balance may have been tipped in some places by the author's own prejudices.

It is a pleasure to express my indebtedness to many people for their generous assistance. I am especially grateful to Drs. S. W. Fox, K. A. Grossenbacher, S. L. Miller, B. Nagy, A. I. Oparin, A. G. Smith, and R. S. Young for the use of illustrations, experimental data, and quotations, and to Drs. S. Akabori, E. Anders, M. Calvin, K. Harada, C. N. Matthews, P. T. Mora, J. Oro', C. Ponnamperuma, C. Sagan, and G. Wald for use of their recent experimental data or quotations.

The library and librarians of the Marine Biological Laboratory at Woods Hole, Massachusetts have been an invaluable aid in literature search. I am also indebted to the Administration of the Newark Beth Israel Hospital for funds and space and particularly to Dr. L. M. Goldman, Director of Laboratories, for his interest and encouragement.

Special thanks are due to Paula Gottdenker, my research assistant, for contributing Chapters one and ten, for the preparation of a number of illustrations, and for the typing of the manuscript. I have also profited greatly in the preparation of this, as of the previous edition, from her criticisms of the first drafts from a reader's point of view.

Series Editor's Statement

In the first edition of this volume I wrote: "The origin of life is one of the oldest problems of mankind, and there have been almost cyclic swings between materialist and other approaches. Professor Keosian is well qualified, as the reader will soon discover, to place all these divergent outlooks in their proper perspective. He has no ax to grind and no doctrine to preach. His only concern is to lay bare in clear and simple, but scholarly, language both his own ideas and those of others." It is gratifying that my views have been so widely shared, alike by professional and lay reader, that a second edition is called for after less than four years.

In this edition Professor Keosian changes neither the nature of his argument nor the force and clarity with which it is presented. He has, however, now divided his material into two parts. The first (Chapters 1–5) presents much the same closely reasoned, and thoroughly documented, account of the historical background, growth, and ultimate formulation of contemporary views. The next five chapters examine in depth the many recent experiments which appear to have given rise to even more problems than they have solved.

I am sure that this second edition will be just as valuable to those who have read the first as it will to those who are here making their first acquaintance with this now classic little monograph.

PETER GRAY

Contents

chapter one

Historical Background

Man, who evolved into the only animal to contemplate himself, must have already, at the dawn of his existence begun to contemplate the world around him, to question the phenomena of his physical surroundings. He looked up at the fixed and yet changing skies; he noted the cycle of seasons; he was aware of death, and he observed life constantly being born and arising spontaneously. When it arose, it could do so in the strangest places, in water, seaweed, mud, and slime, in rotting wood, wounds, carcasses, and filth. Dating back to time immemorial, these weird notions were unhesitatingly accepted until fairly recent times, and not only by senseless and ignorant people. The Greek philosophers and theorists, who stressed the value of exact observation, were as strongly convinced as everybody else that lifeless decaying matter could turn into living things if dampened by rain and warmed by the sun.

Aristotle (384–322 B.C.), who was so great a naturalist that some of his observations in biology remain valid to this day, and whose writings set the scientific climate for 2000 years, also described instances of spontaneous generation, suggesting that even man might arise in this way, though only as a worm to start with. The Roman poet-philosopher Lucretius (ca. 95–55 B.C.) wrote similarly that "many animals spring forth from the earth, formed by rain and the heat of the sun."

Then came a period when Western science had only a tenuous foothold in secluded cloisters, and Aristotle's and other classic writings lay moldering for want of eyes who could read the language. Superstitions, on the other hand, continued to flourish in the popular mind, and beclouded as well the scholastic efforts which began to make their imprint on European learning. Travelers fed the imagination with tales of succulent lambs that grew on gourds of Tartary (Fig. 1-1), and of geese that sprang from the fruit of certain trees in the north of Scotland (Fig. 1-2) and thus making a most welcome Lenten fare.

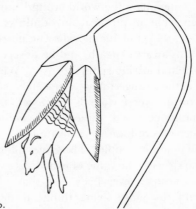

Fig. 1-1. Vegetable Lamb.

Eventually, some of the Greek scientific heritage became accessible again through translations from the Arabic, and the Renaissance movement was unearthing more and more of the treasures of the past. Dissenters began to attack the rigid "Aristotelianism" which had been imposed by the scholastics, but they still could not rid themselves of the old superstitions. Paracelsus (1493–1541), dissented so vehemently that he once burned the books of his predecessors, and often was successful in his chemical treatment of diseases; yet he set down a detailed prescription for the making of a homunculus, a miniature human being. His avowed fol-

Fig. 1-2. Goose Tree.

lower van Helmont (1577–1644), who is credited with the first quantitative experiment, among other achievements, went into self-induced trances to concoct recipes for the production of mice and scorpions (as if anybody needed more of what was already in ample supply). The famous English physician William Harvey (1578–1657), whose revolutionary work on the circulation of the blood (*De motu cordis et sanguinis*, 1628) contributed to the foundation of modern physiology, remained Aristotelian in his acceptance of the spontaneous generation of worms and insects.

✱Little by little, however, the belief in the grosser aspects of spontaneous generation was abandoned, and Redi's well-known experiments (1668)[1] are said to have dealt the first serious blow to the old doctrine.✱ The Florentine physician Francesco Redi (1621–1697) set out to prove his suspicion that flies deposited the eggs from which grew the maggots that lived in rotting meat. He succeeded admirably, but continued to believe that galls generated the larvae of gall-flies, a belief also held by Marcello Malpighi. By 1700 Antonio Vallisnieri had exploded that myth, and other experimenters provided evidence that fleas and lice were also bred from their parents, not from foreign matter. It is debatable whether the separate and not too numerous experimental refutations of the spontaneous origin of some macroorganisms from extraneous sources were indeed responsible for the routing of the firmly entrenched hypothesis. What seems more plausible is that the increasing awareness of biological structures and processes began to throw light into the darkest corners of the long-ingrained beliefs.

A new hurdle arose, however, when the flea-glass, a clumsy tool in the hands of the earliest microscopists, and a fashionable toy and conversation piece in society, came of age. Antony van Leeuwenhoek (1632–1723), whose consuming passion was microscopy, found great delight in refining and improving his single-lens instruments to such an extent that in 1683 he reported having seen structures which could only have been microorganisms. These, he insisted, had entered into his infusions from the air, and his admirer and fellow-microscopist Louis Joblot proved this contention experimentally in 1718.[2] However, to most of the other eighteenth century scientists the enlarged vision afforded by the microscope gave only added proof that spontaneous generation existed after all, as shown by the "sudden" appearance of microorganisms in raindrops and infusions. Foremost among them was the Welsh priest John Needham (1713–1781).[3] He filled flasks with boiling mutton broth and stoppered them tightly, precautions which he thought sufficient to kill any organisms in the broth and to avoid contamination from the outside. In a few days, however, the liquid was full of germs. The same thing happened, of course, with other test infusions, and it seemed to him that there was no other explanation for this but spontaneous generation. In this belief he was ardently supported by a French naturalist, the Comte de Buffon (1707–1788), who also looked for special "life-forces" which engendered living things.

Needham's Italian counterpart, the Abbé Lazzaro Spallanzani (1729-1799) was not satisfied with the proposition that two minutes of boiling would kill all the organisms in the broth, and he succeeded in showing that the fluid in his hermetically sealed flasks, which had been boiled for about 45 minutes, remained sterile.[4] This was the most impressive attack yet against the bacterial aspects of spontaneous generation. The sarcastic wit of the French writer Voltaire entered into the controversy through a pamphlet (1769) ridiculing the "eels" that grew in Needham's mutton broth and lauding Spallanzani's work. In addition, the experiments are said to have inspired the chef and candymaker Nicolas Appert to use the airtight heating method for canning food. Napoleon I, whose troops had suffered from spoiled provisions, showed his gratitude by awarding Appert a prize for his invention (1809).

But even these proofs were not conclusive. Objections were raised on the grounds that life-giving oxygen had been excluded from the hermetically sealed vessels. The German physiologist Theodor Schwann (1810-1882) devised a way to introduce heated air into the boiled broth, and it remained sterile. Other German scientists varied the experiments by purifying the air in strong sulfuric acid or filtering it through sterilized gun cotton. However, their results were frequently equivocal.

The controversy remained at a low ebb until 1859 when the director of the Museum of Natural History in Rouen, Prof. Félix Pouchet (1800-1872), published his findings based on an enormous number of experiments,[5] which in essence reinforced Needham's work. In this publication he reiterated that life could arise in the presence of putrescible matter and a life force, and denied that microorganisms

could be air-borne. The argument was picked up and grew
ever more heated until finally the Académie des Sciences
offered a prize for the final resolution of the controversy.
Louis Pasteur (1822–1895) was convinced that he would be
able to disprove Pouchet and the doctrine of spontaneous
generation.* His first approach was to show that the air did
contain microorganisms. He achieved this by prolonged
filtration of air through gun cotton, dissolving the cotton,
and observing that the solution was full of germs. Then, like
Schwann before him, he heated the air which re-entered the
sterilized test liquids (Fig. 1-3). Finally, in order to avoid

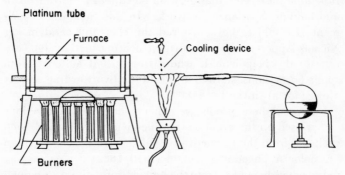

*Fig. 1-3. Apparatus for Sterilizing Air. Cooling device cools the hot air
before entry into the flask.*

the objection that the "life-principle" in the air had been
destroyed by heat, he used swan-necked flasks (Fig. 1-4)
which allowed the untreated air to enter, but trapped any
dust particles before they could fall into the sterile solutions.
As long as the necks of these flasks remained intact nothing
would grow in the liquids. The academicians could only
applaud when Pasteur proclaimed: ... "Never will the doc-

*In a letter to Chappuis (Jan. 1860): "I am hoping to mark a decisive
step very soon by solving, without the least confusion, the celebrated question of spontaneous generation."

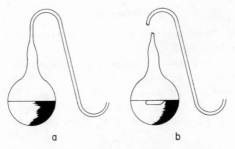

Fig. 1-4. Flasks with S-shaped Necks. (a) Unbroken neck; contents of flask uncontaminated. (b) Flask with broken neck; contents of flask contaminated.

trine of spontaneous generation recover from the mortal blow of this simple experiment."[6]

Thus the controversy about the possibility of the spontaneous origin of organisms seemed to have come full circle from the "first blow" of Redi to the "mortal blow" of Pasteur. However, Pasteur had not disproved spontaneous generation; he merely proved that life could not originate from certain materials and in certain ways. He himself indicated this at a later date (1878) when he said: "Spontaneous generation? I have been looking for it for 20 years, but I have not yet found it, although I do not think that it is an impossibility."[7] A handful of other researchers also thought it possible. There was the physician H. Charlton Bastian,[8] in particular, whose conception of the stepwise chemical evolution of life anticipates Oparin. The results of his experiments, however, were not convincing.

The question of the origin of life is still waiting for a conclusive answer; however, because of the renewed experimental attack of the last 15 years, which was inspired by the theories of J. B. S. Haldane (1892-1964) and A. I. Oparin (1894-), the solution to this age-old puzzle does seem more within reach than ever before.

References

1. F. Redi, "Esperienze intorno alla generazione degl'insetti," Firenze, Italy, 1668.
2. L. Joblot, *Descriptions et usages de plusieurs nouveaux microscopes*, Paris, 1718.
3. J. T. Needham, *Phil. Trans.*, No. 490, (1749) p. 615.
4. L. Spallanzani, *Saggio di osservazioni microscopiche concernenti il sistema della generazione dei sig. di Needham e Buffon*, Modena, Italy, 1765.
5. F. A. Pouchet, *Hétérogénie ou traité de la génération spontanée, basée sur des nouvelles expériences*, Paris, 1859.
6. R. Vallery-Radot, *The Life of Pasteur*, Dover Publications, Inc., New York, 1960, p. 109.
7. J. Nicolle, *Louis Pasteur*, Fawcett Publications, Inc., Greenwich, Conn., 1961, p. 66.
8. H. C. Bastian, *The Beginnings of Life*, D. Appleton & Co., New York, 1872, p. VIII.

chapter two

Nature of the Problem

The thinking on the origin of life had incorporated several main approaches by the turn of the twentieth century. Among these approaches were vitalism, special creation, panspermia, meteorite transfer, mechanism, and materialism. Vitalism attributes the distinctive properties characteristic of living things to a supernatural "life force," and special creation is the literal interpretation of Genesis. Neither concept is susceptible to experimental proof. Panspermia sidesteps the question of the actual origin of life by assuming its eternal and universal existence. Vitalism, special creation, and panspermia need no detailed consideration here. The meteorite transfer theory has been revived recently and will be discussed in Chapter 9.

MECHANISM

Mechanistic theories are based on the belief that the origin, properties, and activities of life derive from the laws of physics and chemistry, and assume that inorganic matter gave rise to a living thing in accordance with those laws. But this approach is confronted with a dilemma. How can a living thing be constructed in the first place from inorganic matter? It was believed that only living things could synthesize organic compounds and that the earth therefore contained no organic compounds in prebiological times. Since organic compounds are essential to living things, the origin of life in the absence of such compounds became a formidable problem—so much so that most scientists long ago took a defeatist attitude toward the possibility of ever finding an answer. Darwin expressed this defeatism in a letter to

J. D. Hooker (1863): "It is mere rubbish thinking at present of the origin of life; one might as well think of the origin of matter."[1] Most of Darwin's contemporaries and many of his followers also dismissed the subject as not worthy of scientific consideration.

The mechanistic hypothesis resolved this quandary by proposing that the first living thing was a living macromolecule, a "moleculobiont," that was formed by the chance coming-together of its constituent elements in the proper proportions and arrangements. It was thought that this was probably a molecule of protein, the class of compound on which life was supposed to depend most intimately. In other words, the mechanistic hypothesis, which clung to the concept that only living things can make organic compounds, explained the origin of the first living thing in terms of the chance combination of the appropriate elements, establishing simultaneously the first organic compound and the first living thing. The mechanists were not discouraged by the enormous span of time required for this chance event. They pointed out that, given enough time, the most improbable event becomes a statistical certainty. A serious shortcoming of the mechanistic hypothesis is its lack of susceptibility to experimental verification. One cannot meaningfully plan an experiment around a hypothesis that depends upon remote accidents.

MATERIALISM

The materialistic hypothesis took a different approach in applying natural laws to the explanation of the origin of life. From the start this theory rejected the contention that only living things could make organic compounds. It proposed that organic compounds were formed abiotically (that is, without the intervention of living things) before organisms came into being. Instead of a chance getting-together of the elements to form a living thing all at once, materialism viewed the origin of life as the result of a series of probable steps of increasing complexity, inevitably leading up to the living state. According to this hypothesis, each successive step resulted in a higher level of organization of matter possessing properties, activities and principles that did not exist at the lower levels. With the advent of organisms, biological principles came into being which did not exist at a lower level of organization. From the materialist view, the origin of life was no remote accident; it was the result of matter evolving to higher and higher levels through the inexorable working out at each level of the inherent potentialities to arrive at the next level.

DEVELOPMENT OF THE MATERIALIST VIEWPOINT

At first this theory did not lend itself to experimentation for want of sufficient advances in physics, chemistry, and allied fields. There were, though, a number of thinkers who started to speculate about the gradual evolution of life from nonliving matter. Among them, to name a few, were F. Engels,[2] H. Spencer,[3] E. Haeckel,[4] H. C. Bastian,[5] B. Moore,[6] E. A. Schäfer,[7] and A. I. Oparin.[8] Engels, in his *Dialectics of Nature*, was among the first to consider the spontaneous generation and the vitalistic theories from a materialist viewpoint. He condemned them both and maintained that life could have resulted only from a continuous evolution of matter, the origin of life being merely a rung in the long ladder of development.

Bastian (1872) enlarged upon this theme thus: "We know that the molecules of elementary or mineral substances combine to form acids and bases by virtue of their own 'inherent' tendencies; that these acids and bases unite so as to produce salts, which, in their turn, will often again combine and give rise to 'double salts.' And at each stage in this series of ascending molecular complexities, we find the products endowed with properties wholly different from those of their constituents. Similarly, amongst the carbon compounds there is abundance of evidence to prove the existence of internal tendencies or molecular properties, which may and do lead to the evolution of more and more complex chemical compounds. And it is such synthetic processes occurring amongst the molecules of colloidal and allied substances, which seem so often to engender or give 'origin' to a kind of matter possessing that subtle combination of properties to which we are accustomed to apply the epithet 'living.'" In a more general vein Schäfer (1912) expressed the same concept: "... setting aside as devoid of scientific foundation the idea of immediate supernatural intervention in the first production of life, we are not only justified in believing, but compelled to believe, that living matter must have owed its origin to causes similar in character to those which have been instrumental in producing all other forms of matter in the universe, in other words, to a process of gradual evolution."

The Russian biochemist Oparin delineated more clearly the materialist hypothesis of the gradual evolution of matter into life. In 1922 he delivered before the Botanical Society in Moscow a communication which dealt with his conclusions concerning the origin of life. He envisioned that organic compounds had already formed on the earth before life arose and that life evolved from these preexisting compounds. Oparin's unique contribution is his revival of the materialistic approach to the question of how life originated, as well as his detailed development of this concept. He views the evolution of matter into inorganic and organic compounds, macromolecules, precells, primitive living things, and higher living forms—not as separate phenomena, but as steps in the unfolding of a single process. Oparin's ideas were first published in 1924 in a booklet entitled *The Origin of Life.*

The concept of the abiotic formation of organic substances in the early prebiological history of the earth was also expressed by J. B. S. Haldane who suggested in 1928, that before the origin of life organic compounds "must have accumulated till the primitive oceans reached the consistency of hot dilute soup."[9] He based this belief on the assumption that the primitive atmosphere contained carbon dioxide, ammonia, and water vapor, but no oxygen. Haldane claimed that such a mixture, exposed to ultraviolet light, would give rise to "a vast variety of organic substances."

The presence of organic compounds established a new order of reactivity not inherent in inorganic compounds. Oparin states: "From this point of view organic chemistry is not simply the chemistry of one of the elements from Mendeleev's periodic table. It exhibits special characteristic regularities which first manifest themselves on passing from the inorganic to the organic compounds of carbon."

Oparin developed his concept logically, supporting his contentions from the findings of many branches of science. He removed the main barriers which obstructed the path and led the way to a scientific attack on the problem. His second, more comprehensive book, *The Origin of Life on Earth*, published in 1936 and translated into English by S. Morgulis in 1938, sparked a renewed interest in the subject. Discussions led to extensive experimentation, and important findings continue to come forth. In spite of this large amount of work, or perhaps because of it, disagreements have arisen. There is general agreement on only one broad point—that organic compounds, abiotically synthesized, preceded the origin of life.

THE PROBLEM OF DEFINITION

A definition of "life" or of "living thing" has been purposely avoided up to this point. Many scientists have expressed the opinion that a precise definition—that is, one which will include all living things, past or present, and will exclude all nonliving things—is not possible. However, this need not be a deterrent to the serious investigation of life and its origin. As Pauling[10] put it: "In connection with the origin of life, I should like to say that it is sometimes easier to study a subject than to define it. For many years I have been studying the nature of the chemical bond .... However, when I discussed this question (with others), we found that it is extremely difficult to define the chemical bond." Life and living thing mean different things to different people. When the comparison involves living things that are very much alive and things that are obviously nonliving, agreement is not difficult to obtain, but at the borderline where the simplest organisms are being compared with complex chemical systems, agreement is generally not possible. Structurally, the simplest form of life to some can consist of a single macromolecule—a "living molecule." Horowitz[11] arrives at such a definition in suggesting that the minimum properties of a living system are mutability, self-duplication, and heterocatalysis. He points out that these criteria are satisfied by the gene which consists of individual molecules of deoxyribonucleic acid.

Some scientists maintain that metabolically the simplest form of life consists of a system in which exergonic (energy-liberating) and endergonic (energy-consuming) reactions are correlated. On the basis of this assumption, one can construct a definition of life, as did K. M. Madison,[12] that will include a system of two inorganic reactions as an organism. Madison proposed that "life is anything perceivable by an observer of a group of chemical systems in which free energy is released as a part of the reactions of one or more of the systems and in which some of this free energy is used in the reactions of one or more of the remaining systems." He recognized that "the definition does not require that the simplest organisms have any organic molecules" and that "things as simple as two inorganic reactions meet the definition."

At the other extreme, a definition of life would include the characteristics of all living things past and present. Thus, no simple definition would be sufficient. For example, a definition of life based on the assumed properties of only the first living things would "exclude from among its features, not merely consciousness, but also respiration, which obviously did not take place among the earliest organisms. On the other hand, if we define life on the basis of phenomena which are typical only of the more highly developed living things, we shall risk relegating the anaerobic bacteria, as well as many primitive organisms to the category of nonliving bodies belonging to inorganic nature." [13]

PERSPECTIVE

This apparent confusion reflects the necessity of recognizing the gradual transition of matter into higher and higher levels of organization embodying newer and more complex properties. One's definition of life may then lead to the acceptance of a particular level of organization of matter as a "living" state but not any level below it, whereas another's definition may accept a different level, either higher or lower, as the starting point. What is important is not an exact definition of life at the borderline, but rather the recognition, of the existence of increasing levels of organization of matter, and the understanding of the mechanisms which operate to bring each of these about. In other words, it would appear more sensible to approach the problem of the origin of life not as an attempt to discover the precise point at which lifeless matter gave rise to the "first living things," but rather as an examination of the mechanisms operating in the transition of matter on this earth to higher and higher levels of organization. Then the first level of organization which can

be considered "alive" will still be a matter of personal pref-
erence, but at least we will all be talking about the same
thing. Thus, as Pirie has pointed out, attempts at an exact
definition of life are not only fruitless, but meaningless.[14]
The reality of this view will be considered more fully in
Chapter 8.

References

1. F. Darwin, *The Life and Letters of Charles Darwin*, Vol. II, D.
   Appleton & Co., New York, 1896, p. 202.
2. F. Engels, *Dialectics of Nature*, International Publishing Company New York, 1940 (translated).
3. H. Spencer, *First Principles*, D. Appleton & Co., New York,
   1864.
4. E. Haeckel, *The Wonders of Life*, Harper & Brothers, New York,
   1905.
5. H. C. Bastian, *The Beginnings of Life*, D. Appleton & Co., New
   York, 1872, p. VIII.
6. B. Moore, *The Origin and Nature of Life*, Henry Holt & Co., New
   York, 1912.
7. E. A. Schäfer, "Presidential Address to the Brit. Assoc. Adv.
   Science,[11] 1912.
8. A. I. Oparin, *The Origin of Life on Earth*, Macmillan, New York,
   1938, (translated by S. Morgulis).
9. J. B. S. Haldane, "Rationalist Annual" (1928), reprinted in
   Science and Human Life, Harper & Brothers, New York, 1933.
10. L. Pauling, in Oparin, A. I. (ed.), *The Origin of Life on the Earth*
    (I.U.B. Sympos. Series, Vol. i), Pergamon Press, New York,
    1959, p. 119.
11. N. H. Horowitz, ibid p. 107.
12. K. M. Madison, "The Organism and Its Origin," *Evolution* **7**,
    211 (1953).
13. A. I. Oparin, *Life: its Nature, Origin and Development*, Academic
    Press, Inc., Publ., New York, 1962 (translated by A. Synge).
14. N. W. Pirie, "The Meaninglessness of the Terms Life and
    Living," in Needham, H., and Green, D., (eds.), *Perspectives in
    Biochemistry*, The University Press, Cambridge, England, 1937.

chapter three

The Origin and Distribution of Organic Compounds

OPARIN HYPOTHESIS*

In his approach to the problem of the origin of organic compounds on the primitive earth, Oparin based his contentions on the then prevalent theory of the fiery origin of the planets. This mode of formation also explained the observed similarity in types and abundances of various elements of the planets and of the sun's atmosphere. Although the fiery origin is no longer considered to be valid, Oparin's hypothesis is essentially sound because the events he envisioned as taking place on a hot earth while it cooled, may have taken place earlier in the cloud of dust and gas[1] which, according to modern theory, later condensed to form the earth. From either approach, then, the composition of the earth's atmosphere would be about the same.

Oparin pointed out that the hydrides of carbon and nitrogen (CH_4 and NH_3, respectively) would form sooner and be more stable than their oxides (CO_2 and NO_2). He not only proposed that the primitive atmosphere contained methane, ammonia, water vapor, hydrogen, and no oxygen, but also gave the chemical details of how this condition could come about. He was emphatic in his belief that this "reducing atmosphere," under the force of ultraviolet radiation and other forms of energy would be the source of large quantities

*This is an abstract of A. I. Oparin's *The Origin of Life*, Dover Publications, Inc., New York, 1953.

of all kinds of organic compounds including biochemically important ones. He subscribed to J. B. S. Haldane's view that the primitive oceans contained so much organic matter that they constituted a "hot dilute soup."

The next stage in Oparin's hypothesis is the separation of colloidal substances from the environmental fluid in the form of microscopic droplets (Fig. 3-1). Such a separation of colloids (coacervation) from a solution had been described earlier by Bungenberg de Jong. Oparin utilized the idea in his hypothesis and considerably enlarged it. He considered the formation of microscopic droplets as the most important aspect of coacervation. A great diversity in composition among such droplets could exist, depending on the local environmental conditions under which they would form. He laid great emphasis on the need for the existence of diversity in chemical composition and physical structure among coacervate droplets.

Diversity is the basis for the operation of natural selection and Oparin believed that a kind of natural selection took place even among these prebiotic structures. The chemically better balanced and physically more stable droplets would

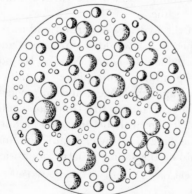

Fig. 3-1. Coacervate Droplets.

"survive" longer and have a longer period in which to develop further. Each droplet would exhibit a chemical behavior determined not only by its original composition and structure but also by the physical and chemical characteristics of the environment. Thus, droplets of different composition in the same environment, or the same kind of droplets in different environments would differ in their chemical behavior. This behavior could render a droplet more "viable" or less "viable." Those that survived the longest could offer a longer duration for the development in them of new reactions and pathways.

The most "successful" droplets would be those which had a coordination between exergonic and endergonic reactions and between degradation and synthesis in which the balance was slightly in favor of synthesis. Such droplets would slowly increase in size, becoming gradually more and more subject to fragmentation by physical disturbances in the environment. Those fragments containing a complement of the chemicals of the parent body would continue the process of "growth," chemical development, and eventual fragmentation. Random fragmentation was gradually replaced by internal mechanisms of splitting, leading eventually to more precise mechanisms of cell division.

In a later edition (*The Origin of Life on the Earth*, Academic Press, New York, 1957) Oparin brought his theory in line with the scientific developments of the intervening period. The theory, however, suffered no essential change thereby, which attests to the soundness of the original concept.

THE UNIVERSAL DISTRIBUTION OF ORGANIC COMPOUNDS

It is now recognized that organic compounds are probably widely distributed throughout the universe, and natural conditions do exist under which these compounds could conceivably be synthesized abiotically. Knowledge of the universe outside of our planet has been gained primarily by observing objects and phenomena in the sky. The information reaches us in the form of electromagnetic waves from these objects. Of the whole electromagnetic spectrum only two portions reach the surface of the earth; the rest are reflected or absorbed by the ionosphere or atmosphere. One portion is represented by the shortwave radio rays with a wavelength between 0.1 millimeter and 32.8 meters. The other is the range between 5×10^{-7} and 1×10^{-6} centimeters which covers the near infrared, the whole visible range, and the near ultraviolet. The spectrum is summarized in Fig. 3-2.

METHODS OF GATHERING DATA

Early observations were limited to the narrow window represented by the visible portion of the spectrum. With the development of better optical telescopes of various types and power, we have been able to reach increasingly farther into the universe. Accessories to the telescope can record phenomena not discernable by eye or can register quantitatively the uncertain approximations of distance, luminosity, etc., detected by eye. The spectroscope is one of the most useful of these accessories. Attached to the telescope, it breaks the incoming light into a visible spectrum. When the spectrum from a region or an object in the universe is analyzed, the presence of specific substances can be inferred.

The use of a camera on a spectroscope makes it possible to record such observations permanently. The use of film, sensitive to ultraviolet or to infrared rays, enables us to detect substances which do not appear on the visible spectrum. Furthermore, the intensity of the respective bands is a measure of the approximate abundances of the substances thus detected.

Radio telescopes have also assisted in unique discoveries. With these instruments, we can look through the second

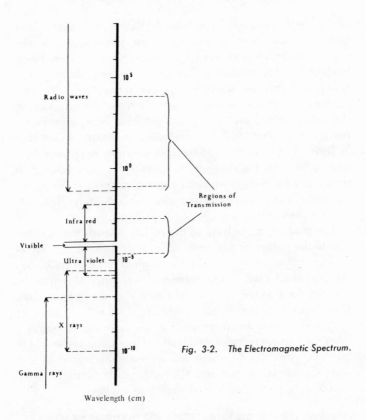

Fig. 3-2. *The Electromagnetic Spectrum.*

"window" depicted in Fig. 3-2 and detect wavelengths in the range of microwaves and short-wave radio waves. Several thousand objects that emit no light but do emit a high intensity of radio waves have been discovered in this way. Before the advent of radio telescopes, these "radio stars" went undetected.

The use of balloons, rockets, and satellites is beginning to overcome further limitations in observing the universe. These limitations are the optically distorting and turbulent character of the atmosphere and the absorption by it of much of the electromagnetic spectrum. Balloons, rockets, and satellites can carry instruments and accessories to the calmer, upper reaches of the atmosphere or completely beyond it. Appropriate rocket-borne devices can intercept rays before they are absorbed by our atmosphere. By this method, x-rays emanating apparently from the direction of the Crab Nebula and of the constellation Scorpio were reported in October 1962 and confirmed by a later rocket shot in June 1963. Great as these contributions have been, the devices that lift instruments into space are still limited in their capacity to carry all the necessary accessories available on land. Eventually, orbiting observatories may eliminate some of these limitations.

The study and analysis of meteorites furnish yet another clue to the nature of the immediate space around us. Meteorites are thought to be derived from material that makes up the asteroidal belt. Urey[2] suggests that while this may be true for the iron meteorites, the moon appears to be a more likely source of the stone meteorites. In either case, the meteorites afford us an opportunity to make direct observations on extra-terrestrial material. This assumption would not be entirely valid if the moon were contaminated by terrestrial material ejected from the earth,[2] or if the moon originated in the first place from the earth by fission.[3]

UNIVERSAL DISTRIBUTIONS OF HYDROCARBONS

We have gained much useful information by the above mentioned means concerning the chemical composition of the stars, galaxies, gas and dust clouds, and interstellar space.[23] There is good reason to believe that in addition to a variety of inorganic matter, the free radicals $:CH$ and $:CH_2$; dicarbon (C_2); the lower hydrocarbons methane (CH_4), ethane (H_3C-CH_3), acetylene $(HC\equiv CH)$, and ethylene $(H_2C=CH_2)$, as well as others are present in stars or in clouds of gas and dust; there is also some evidence of higher hydrocarbons. Compounds of carbon and nitrogen, such as cyanogen (CN), are also detected.

Hydrocarbons have been found to exist also on planets of our solar system. Methane is detected on Jupiter, Uranus, Neptune, and on Saturn and its satellite Titan. Although most of the carbon in the atmosphere of Venus, earth, and Mars is in the form of carbon dioxide, methane has been detected on Venus and Mars. Ethylene and acetylene have been detected on Jupiter. Ethylene and acetylene have also been detected in the atmosphere of Venus and Mars. Hydrocarbons still form abiogenically on the earth by the action of hot water on metal carbides or of cold water on hot carbides extruded by volcanic action.

Meteorites furnish direct evidence of the chemical composition of extraterrestrial bodies.[4-22] The presence of complex hydrocarbons in certain meteorites has been unequivocally established. As long ago as 1834 Berzelius found carbonaceous material in the Alais meteorite. Recent analyses of a sample of the Orgueil meteorite, which fell at Orgueil, France in 1864, show it to contain 6 per cent organic material in addition to a number of inorganic compounds.

Nagy, Meinschein, and Hennessy,[4] reported in 1961 the presence of saturated hydrocarbons containing 15 or more carbon atoms as well as mono-, di-, and tetracycloalkanes (Table 3-1). They found that the composition and characteristics of these hydrocarbons were similar enough to hydrocarbons in butter and in recent sediments to justify the conclusion that ". . . the composition of the hydrocarbons in the Orgueil meteorite provide evidence for biogenic activity." This was an historic paper, for it precipitated renewed interest in and analyses of meteoritic composition and origin. Further findings by various investigators have been reported for long-chain fatty acids,[5] lipids, open-chain organic sulfides and S-containing heterocyclic compounds,[6-8] porphyrin or porphyrin derivatives,[9] purines, pyrimidines, and their de-

TABLE 3-1

Tetracycloalkanes Carbon Number	Peak Heights of Saturated Hydrocarbons in		
	Butter	Recent Sediments	Meteorite
15	218	243	231
16	245*	437*	578*
17	215	283	302
18	141	216	230
19	108	161	99
20	117*	117	70
21	65	86	46
22	50	87*	39
23	43	85	45
24	41	129*	56*
25	34	79	50
26	35	67	44
27	59	101*	53*
28	59	100	46
29	68*	135*	29

*Peaks larger than the peaks of their homologs which contain either one more or one less carbon atoms (that is, peaking).

rivatives,[10-11] amino acids,[12] and pristane, phytane, and other hydrocarbons.[13] Claims have been made by some, and refuted by others, that some, if not all of the organic compounds identified in the carbonaceous chondrites, are of biologic origin. Even greater heat has been generated by the reported findings of fossil microorganisms,[14-22] and of optical activity[6] in some of the organic compounds in the carbonaceous chondrites. Although this controversy has yet to be resolved, most agree that organic compounds found in fair abundance and complexity in carbonaceous chondrites do not represent contamination but are in fact indigenous.

Organic compounds seem, indeed, to be universally distributed. They are detected not only in stellar material but also in interstellar space, and mainly under conditions that preclude the possibility of their origin from living things.

References
1. M. H. Studier, R. Hayatsu, and E. Anders, *Science* **149,** 1455 (1965).

2. H. C. Urey, *Science* **147**, 1262, (1965).
3. G. J. F. MacDonald, *Ann. N. Y. Acad. Sci.* **118**, 739 (1965) (see esp. pp. 772–775).
4. B. Nagy, W. G. Meinschein, and D. J. Hennessy, *Ann. N. Y. Acad. Sci.* **93**, 25 (1961).
5. B. Nagy and Sister M. Bitz, *Arch. Biochem. Biophys.* **101**, 240 (1963).
6. B. Nagy, Sister M. Murphy, V. E. Modzeleski, G. Rouser, G. Claus, D. J. Hennessy, U. Colombo, and F. Gazzarrini, *Nature* **202**, 228 (1964).
7. Sister M. Murphy, B. Nagy, G. Rouser, and G. Kritchevsky, *J. Am. Oil Chemists Soc.* **42**, 475 (1965).
8. Sister M. Murphy and B. Nagy, *J. Am. Oil Chemists Soc.* **43**, 189 (1966).
9. G. W. Hodgson and B. C. Baker, *Nature* **202**, 125 (1964).
10. M. Calvin, *Chem. Eng. News* **39**, 96 (1961).
11. R. Hayatsu, *Science* **146**, 1291 (1964).
12. I. R. Kaplan, E. T. Degens, and J. H. Reuter, *Geochim. Cosmochim. Acta* **27**, 805 (1963).
13. J. Oró, D. W. Nooner, A. Zlatkis, and S. A. Wikström, cited in H. C. Urey, *Science* **151**, 163 (1966).
14. G. Claus and B. Nagy, *Nature* **192**, 594 (1961).
15. B. Nagy, K. Fredriksson, J. Kudynowski, and L. Carlson, *Nature* **200**, 565 (1933).
16. G. Claus, B. Nagy, and D. L. Europa, *Ann. N. Y. Acad. Sci.* **108**, 580 (1963).
17. B. Nagy, G. Claus, and D. J. Hennessy, *Nature* **193**, 1129 (1962).
18. B. Nagy, K. Fredriksson, H. C. Urey, G. Claus, C. A. Andersen, and J. Percy, *Nature* **198**, 121 (1963).
19. P. Palik, *Nature* **194**, 1065 (1962).
20. G. Claus and Eva A. Suba-C., *Nature* **204**, 118 (1964).
21. G. Mamikunian and M. H. Briggs, *Nature* **197**, 1245 (1963).
22. "Life-forms in Meteorites and the Problem of Terrestrial Contamination: A Study in Methodology," *Ann. N. Y. Acad. Sci.* **105**, 927 (1964).
23. "Cosmic Dust," Proc. of a Conference on Cosmic Dust, *Ann. N. Y. Acad. Sci.* **119**, 1–368 (1964).

chapter four

Abiotic Synthesis of Organic Compounds

The concept of the abiotic formation of organic compounds has become almost universally accepted in the last decade or so. The synthesis under simulated primitive earth conditions of many biologically important compounds, (and some organic compounds not associated with living things) has been reported (See Table 4-2). We tend to give more weight and consideration to the biologically significant compounds and less consideration to the biologically nonsignificant ones. This tendency is only natural, but it may be a deviation from the central aim of determining how the first living things originated from inanimate beginnings. In this context the question arises: Were the first living things recognizable biochemical systems in present-day terms? In answer, it is widely assumed that the metabolism of the first living things was similar to the fermentative metabolism of present-day "primitive" anaerobic bacteria. The validity of this assumption will be considered in chapter 8.

The purpose of this chapter is to acquaint the reader with some of the main lines of experimental attack on the problem and with the types of compounds that have been reported as synthesized under simulated primitive earth conditions. The latter term refers to the conditions that are presumed to have existed on the earth several billion years ago when organic compounds began to be formed. There is no general agreement on what constitutes "primitive earth conditions," and the diversity of reaction mixtures and energy sources listed in Table 4-2 reflects the dissension. The controversy will be considered in Chapter 6.

METHODS AND APPARATUS

In general an investigator takes substances which he assumes were the precursors of primitive organic compounds and places them in an apparatus designed to simulate and maintain the presumed primitive earth conditions. The mixture is then energized for a given length of time that varies according to the nature of the experiment and the ideas of

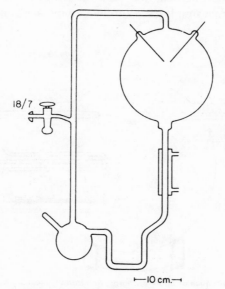

Fig. 4-1. Spark-discharge Apparatus. From S. L. Miller, J. Am. Chem. Soc. **77**, 2351 (1955).

the investigator. In many cases the energy source is chosen as a matter of convenience since it appears that any type of energy—electricity, ultrasonics, hypersonics, radiation of various kinds and sources: heat, sun light, artificial light, ultraviolet, x- and gamma radiation, radiation from the decay of radioactive elements—is effective when applied in sufficient intensity and quantity.

Electric sparking seems to be one of the energy sources easier to apply and control and was the source that Miller used in his now classical experiments of 1953 and 1955. The apparatus he used (Fig. 4-1) has been modified more or less by other investigators to suit specific requirements, e.g., Fig. 4-2. The use of high energy radiation requires a greater modification of apparatus as shown in Figs. 4-3 and 4-4.

Sidney W. Fox, who has reported the synthesis of "proteinoids" from simple gases through amino acids in one con-

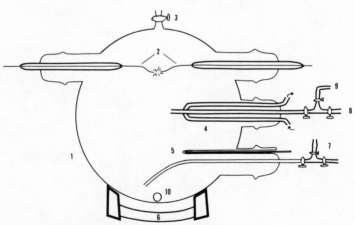

Fig. 4-2. *Modification of Spark-discharge Apparatus. From K. A. Grossenbacher and C. A. Knight, "Origins of Prebiological Systems and of their Molecular Matrices," Academic Press, New York, 1965.*

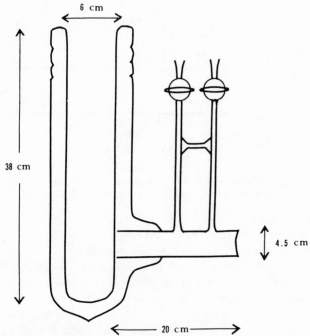

Fig. 4-3. *Apparatus for the Irradiation of Solid Methane* $-C^{14}$, *Ammonia and Water with 5 Mev electrons. After J. Oro, Nature* **197**, 971 (1963).

tinuous procedure, has been a strong advocate of thermal synthesis of organic compounds.

The first experiments in this century specifically aimed at the question of the chemical origin of life were those reported by Calvin and his co-workers.[56] By bombarding carbonic acid with 40 Mev helium ions from a cyclotron, they obtained formaldehyde and formic acid. Oxygen was present, so the starting mixture was an oxidizing rather than a reducing medium. Regarding this point, Urey[66] wrote "This experiment is important in that it induced a reexamination

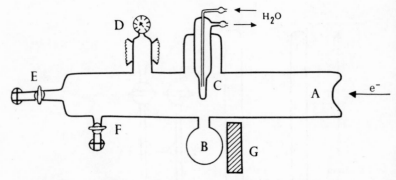

Fig. 4-4. *Apparatus for Electron Irradiation of Methane Ammonia and Water. After Ponnamperuma et al. Proc. Nat. Acad. Sci.* **49,** 737 (1963a).

of Oparin's hypothesis of the reducing atmosphere." Calvin's later experiments with ionizing radiation were with a reducing mixture and were highly productive.

Urey had been engaged in speculations regarding the origin and development of the planets and had corroborated Oparin's hypothesis of the reducing composition of the earth's primitive atmosphere.[67] This hypothesis was put to a test in 1953 by Stanley L. Miller,[1,2] who was then Urey's student. Using the apparatus diagrammed in Fig. 4-1, he passed a continuous spark through a circulating mixture of methane, ammonia, hydrogen and steam for a period of days. This resulted in a surprisingly large array and amount of organic compounds as later analyses showed (Table 4-1). There soon followed numerous experiments by various investigators which confirmed the relative ease of obtaining organic compounds from a simple carbon source as long as reducing conditions prevail and a suitable energy source is applied.

Table 4-2 is arranged as a summary of the compounds synthesized, and the reagents and energies employed. Consequently, the work of any one investigator may be listed in

TABLE 4-1   Yields of Compounds (Moles × 10^5)

	Spark Run1	Silent Discharge Run 3	N_2 Run Run 6
Glycine	63 (2.1)*	80 (0.46)*	14.2 (0.48)*
Alanine	34	9	1.0
Sarcosine	5	86	1.5
β-Alanine	15	4	7.0
α-Aminobutyric acid	5	1	—
N-Methylalanine	1	12.5	—
Aspartic acid	0.4	0.2	0.3
Glutamic acid	0.6	0.5	0.5
Iminodiacetic acid	5.5	0.3	3.9
Imino-acetic-propionic acid	1.5	—	—
Formic acid	233	149	135
Acetic acid	15.2	135	41
Propionic acid	12.6	19	22
Glycolic acid	56	28	32
Lactic acid	31	4.3	1.5
α-Hydroxybutyric acid	5	1	—
Succinic acid	3.8	—	2
Urea	2	—	2
Methylurea	1.5	—	0.5
Sum of yields of compounds listed	15%	3%	8%

*Per cent yield of glycine, based on carbon placed in the apparatus as methane.
S. L. Miller in Oparin A. I., (ed.), "The Origin of Life on the Earth" (I.U.B. Sympos. Series), Pergamon Press, New York, 1959.

several different places if he reported more than one class of compound. This information can be readily assembled, however, since all of the references bearing the same number pertain to one paper.

The list in Table 4-2 gives impressive evidence of the strides that have been made in a little more than a dozen years toward a naturalistic explanation of the origin of life. Not many years ago this was a question long abandoned by scientists as unsolvable; biology books were silent on the subject. Today the problem is being attacked vigorously in all its many aspects. Numerous meetings at local, national, and international levels have been held on the subject and

TABLE 4-2.[a]

Amino Acids

Compounds Synthesized	Reaction Mixture	Energy Source	Author	Year	Ref.#
Taking all the reports together, the following amino acids have been reported in the order of diminishing frequency:	CH_4, NH_3, H_2, H_2O	electric sparking	S. L. Miller	1953	1
	$(CH_2O)_x$, $FeCl_3$, KNO_3	bright sunlight	K. Bahadur	1955	2
	NH_4 malate, NH_4 fumarate	heat	S. W. Fox, et al.	1954	3
Alanine, aspartic acid, glycine, glutamic acid, beta-alanine, lysine, serine, valine, arginine, histidine, proline, ornithine, isoleucine, leucine, threonine, asparagine. When hydrogen sulfide was used in the gas mixture, derivatives of cysteine were reported.	CH_4, NH_3, H_2O			1955	4
	CO, H_2, N_2, H_2O	electric sparking	P. H. Abelson	1956	5
	CO_2, NH_3, H_2, H_2O			1956	6
	CH_4, NH_3, H_2, H_2O				
	NH_4 acetate (1% or 2.5%)	electric sparking	L. Hough, et al.	1956	7
	CH_4, NH_3, H_2, H_2S	beta-rays	T. Hasselstrom, et al.	1957	8
	$(CH_2O)_x$, molybdenum oxide	electric sparking	K. Heyns, et al.	1957	9
	H_2CO, NH_2OH	500 W bulb at 45 cm	K. Bahadur, et al.	1958	10
In many cases the amino acids did not form in the free state but were obtained on hydrolysis of undefined polymers, which are usually formed in these experiments.	CH_4 (or CO), NH_3, H_2O H_2CO, NH_4NO_3, (or NH_4Cl) NH_3, HCN				
	KNO_3, KNO_2, NH_2OH; + citric or + glutamic acid, or + glucose	heat (70–100°C)	J. Oro', et al.	1959	11
	malic acid, urea	electric sparking	T. E. Pavloskaya, et al.	1959	12
	NH_3, HCN, H_2O	ultraviolet heat (70°C)	J. Oro', et al.	1961	13
The absence of phenylalanine, tyrosine, and tryptophan may be due to their destruction on hydrolysis of the polymer, or to their		ultraviolet	G. Ferrari, et al.	1961	14
		heat	S. W. Fox	1961	15
		heat (70–100°C)	J. Oro'	1963	16

presence in quantities too small for detection.	NH₃, CH₄ (or C₂H₆)	ultraviolet	C. U. Lowe, et al.	1963	17
	NH₃, HCN	heat (90°C)	K. Harada, et al.	1965	18
	CH₄, NH₃, H₂O	heat (1000°C)	K. A. Grossenbacher, et al.	1965	19
	NH₃, H₂O, CH₄, H₂ cyanoacetylene, NH₃, HCN	electric spark heat (100°C)	R. A. Sanchez, et al.	1966	20
Amino Acid Derivatives and Precursors					
aminonitriles, amides	aldehydes, HCN, NH₃, H₂O	heat	J. Oro'	1963	16
aminonitriles	HCN		J. P. Ferris, et al.	1965	21
cysteic acid, cystamine, taurine	CH₄, NH₄OH, H₂S	electrons, 10^9 rads	A. S. Chougal, et al.	1966	22
formamidine, glycinamide	NH₃, HCN, H₂O	heat (30°–100°C)	J. Oro'	1961	23
aminonitrile	CH₄, NH₃	corona discharge	F. Woeller, et al.	1966	24
sarcosine	CH₄, NH₃, H₂O, H₂	electric sparking	S. L. Miller	1953	1
				1955	2
sarcosine	H₂O, CH₄, NH₃ CO₂, NH₃, H₂, H₂O	electric sparking	P. H. Abelson	1956	5
Small Peptides					
peptides	n-carboxyamino acid anhydrides		R. R. Becker, et al.	1953	25
glycyl-glycine, glycyl-diglycine	aminoacetonitrile sulfate, kaolin	heat (120°–140°C)	H. Hanafusa, et al.	1959	26
various dipeptides	corresponding amino acids, dicyandiamide	ultraviolet	G. Steinman, et al.	1964	27
diglycine	glycine, dicyandiamide, HCl	spontaneous	G. Steinman, et al.	1965	28
glycylglycine, dileucine	glycine, leucine, H₂O, cyanamide	ultraviolet	C. Ponnamperuma, et al.	1965	29
glycylglycylglycine, glycylleucine					
dialanine	alanine, HCl, dicyandiamide	spontaneous	G. Steinman, et al.	1965	30
Polypeptides					
polypeptides	tripeptides, polyphosphoric acid esters	heat (50°–60°C)	G. Schramm, et al.	1958	31
				1962	32

TABLE 4-2. (continued)

Compounds Synthesized	Reaction Mixture	Energy Source	Author	Year	Ref. #
(Polypeptides, continued)					
proteinoid	18 amino acids	heat	S. W. Fox, et al.	1958	33
polypeptide	CH_4, NH_3, H_2O	electric discharge	C. Ponnamperuma, et al.	1966	34
				1966	35
Purines, Pyrimidines, Derivatives, Nucleotides					
adenine, guanine	CH_4, NH_3, H_2O or HCN	beta-rays linear acceleration	C. Ponnamperuma	1966	36
adenosine, AMP, ADP, ATP, A4P	adenine, ribose, EtMtP	ultraviolet	C. Ponnamperuma, et al.	1963	39
				1965	46
AMP, GMP, CMP, UMP, TMP	NaH_2PO_4 + ribosides	heat (160°C)	C. Ponnamperuma, et al.	1965	37
adenosine triphosphate—ATP	ADP, Kaolin	spontaneous	G. Steinman, et al.	1965	30
adenosine	ribose, adenine, PPE	heat (50°–60°C)	G. Schramm, et al.	1962	32
adenosine monophosphate-AMP	adenosine, OP, dicyandiamide	ultraviolet	G. Steinman, et al.	1964	27
adenine, guanine, hypoxanthine	HCN, HN_3	heat (90°C)	C. U. Lowe, et al.	1963	17
deoxyadenosine	adenine, deoxyribose, CN^-	ultraviolet or spontaneous	C. Ponnamperuma, et al.	1964	38
AMP, ADP, ATP, A4P	AR, AMP, ADP + EtMtP	ultraviolet	C. Ponnamperuma, et al.	1963	39
				1965	46
guanine	CH_4, NH_3, H_2O	heat	C. Ponnamperuma, et al.	1963	40
cytosine	cyanoacetylene, KCN, H_2O	heat (100°C) one day	R. A. Sanchez, et al.	1966	20
guanylurea	alanine, HCl, dicyandiamide	spontaneous	G. Steinman, et al.	1965	30
adenine, guanine	HCN	ultraviolet	C. Ponnamperuma, et al.	1963	41
adenine	CH_4, NH_3, H_2O	4.5 Mev electrons	C. Ponnamperuma, et al.	1963	42
uracil	NH_3, CH_4, H_2O or malic acid + PPA	heat	S. W. Fox, et al.	1961	15

34

adenine	NH_3, CN^-, H_2O	heat (90°C)	J. Oro'	1960	43
4-amino-5-cyanimidazole,	NH_3, HCN, H_2O	heat (30°–100°C)	J. Oro', et al.	1961	44
4-aminoimidazole-5-carboxamide			J. Oro'	1960	43
4-amino-5-cyanimidazole	aminomalanonitrile		J. Oro', et al.	1961	44
4-aminoimidazole-5-carboxamide			J. P. Ferris, et al.	1965	21
UpU, UpUp	uridine, NaH_2PO_4	160°C, 2 hours	C. Ponnamperuma, et al.	1965	45
nucleosides, nucleotides	purines, ribose, deoxyribose, phosphate	ultraviolet	C. Ponnamperuma	1966	36

Polynucleotides

polynucleotides	nucleotides, PPE	heat (50°–60°C)	G. Schramm, et al.	1962	32
polyuridylic acid	uridine-2'(3')-phosphate, PPE	heat	N. K. Kochetkov, et al.	1964	47
polycytidylic acid	3'(2')-cytidylic acid, PPA	heat (65°C)	A. W. Schwartz, et al.	1965	48
polyuridylic acid	uridylic acid, PPE	heat	G. Schramm	1966	49

Other Nitrogenous Compounds

N-methyl-alanine,	CH_4, NH_3, H_2, H_2O	electric sparking	S. L. Miller	1953	1
alpha-amino-*n*-butyric acid				1955	2
urea, methylurea,	CH_4, NH_3, H_2O, H_2	electric sparking	S. L. Miller	1953	1
iminodiacetic acid				1955	2
alpha-amino-*n*-butyric acid	CH_4, NH_3, H_2, H_2O	electric sparking	L. Hough, et al.	1956	7
urea, ethanolamine	CH_4, NH_3, H_2, H_2O	electric sparking	L. Hough, et al.	1956	7
n-methyl-alanine,	CH_4, NH_3, H_2, H_2S	electric sparking	K. Heyns, et al.	1957	9
alpha-amino-*n*-butyric acid					
thiourea, thioacetamide,	CH_4, NH_3, H_2, H_2S	electric sparking	K. Heyns, et al.	1957	9
thiocyanate					
urea, acetamide, acetone	CH_4, NH_3, H_2O (−383°F)	protons – 60' cyclot.	R. Berger	1961	50
alpha-amino-butyric acid,	citric acid, KNO_3, KNO_2, NH_2, OH; or glutaric acid + above	ultraviolet	G. Ferrari, et al.	1961	14

TABLE 4-2. (continued)

Compounds Synthesized	Reaction Mixture	Energy Source	Author	Year	Ref. #
(Other Nitrogenous Compounds, continued)					
urea	CH_4, NH_3, H_2O, H_2	5 Mev electrons, linear acceleration	C. Palm, et al.	1962	51
cyanoacetylene	CH_4, N_2	electric discharge	R. A. Sanchez, et al.	1966	20
Other Polymers					
unidentified polymers	CH_4, NH_3, H_2O, H_2	electric sparking	S. L. Miller	1953	1
				1955	2
polymers	amino acid amides	heat (100°C)	J. Oro', et al.	1960	52
unidentified polymers	NH_3, HCN	heat (90°C)	C. U. Lowe, et al.	1963	17
co-polymers	various monomers	heat	C. Ponnamperuma, et al.	1963	40
polymers (polymeric cyanide)	NH_3, H_2O, CH_4, H_2	electric spark	K. A. Grossenbacher, et al.	1965	19
polymers giving several amino acids upon hydrolysis	CH_4, NH_3, H_2O	electric discharge	C. Ponnamperuma, et al.	1966	35
Aldehydes, Ketones, Sugars					
$C_3 - C_6$ sugars	HCN, NH_3, H_2O	heat (30°–100°C)	J. Oro'	1961	23
2-deoxyribose	formaldehyde + acetaldehyde; glyceraldehyde + acetaldehyde		J. Oro', et al.	1962	53
disaccharides	glucose, dicyandiamide	ultraviolet	G. Steinman, et al.	1964	27
glucose-6-phosphate	glucose, phosphoric acid, dicyandiamide	spontaneous or ultraviolet	G. Steinman, et al.	1964	27
ribose, deoxyribose	formaldehyde or HCN; formaldehyde, H_2O	beta-rays lin. accel. ultraviolet or gamma rays	C. Ponnamperuma	1966	36

36

Polysaccharides

polyglycoside	glucose, PPE	heat (50°–60°C)	G. Schramm, et al.	1962	32
fructose polymers	fructose, PPE	heat (50°–60°C)	G. Schramm, et al.	1962	32
ribose polymers	ribose, PPE	heat	G. Schramm, et al.	1962	32
glucose polymers	glucose, phosphoric acid	heat (140°–170°C)	P. T. Mora	1965	54

Organic Acids — C_{12} Acids

acetic, propionic, lactic, glycollic, formic, succinic, alpha-hydroxybutyric	CH_4, NH_3, H_2, H_2O_2	electric sparking	S. L. Miller	1953 / 1955	1 / 2
formic, glycollic, lactic	CH_2, NH_2OH, H_2O	heat (70°–100°C)	J. Oro', et al.	1959	11
acetic, malic	CH_4, NH_3, H_2O	heat	S. W. Fox, et al.	1961	15
monocarboxylic acids, C_2–C_{12}	CH_4, H_2O	semicorona discharge	W. A. Allen, et al.	1966	55

Simple Compounds

formaldehyde, formic acid	CO_2, H_2O, H_2, Fe^{++}	40 million electron volts, Helium ions	W. M. Garrison, et al.	1951	56
HCN	CH_4, NH_3, H_2O, H_2	electric sparking	S. L. Miller	1953 / 1955	1 / 2
HCN	CH_4, NH_3, H_2O, H_2	electric sparking	L. Hough, et al.	1956	7
HCN	CH_4, NH_3, H_2O, H_2	electric sparking	T. E. Pavlovskaya, et al.	1959	12
ammonia	N_2, H_2	ultrasonic vibration	I. E. Elpiner, et al.	1959	57
formaldehyde, HCN	H_2O, CO, H_2, N_2	beta-rays lin. accel.	C. Ponnamperuma	1966	36
HCN, formaldehyde	CH_4, NH_3, H_2O	spontaneous	T. Waldsten, et al.	1959	58
HCN dimers	HCN, OH^-	ultraviolet	C. Sagan, et al.	1960	59
formaldehyde	CH_4, NH_3, H_2O, H_2	35°C waterbath	S. L. Miller, et al.	1964	60
pyrophosphate	$CaCl_2$, NaH_2PO_4, KCNO	ultraviolet	G. Steinman, et al.	1965	30
pyrophosphate	orthophosphate, dicyandiamide, kaolin				
dicyandiamide	cyanide solutions or CH_4, NH_3, H_2O	ultraviolet or electron beam	A. Schimpel, et al.	1965	61

TABLE 4-2. (continued)

Compounds Synthesized	Reaction Mixture	Energy Source	Author	Year	Ref. #
(Simple Compounds, continued)					
NH_3	H_2, H_2O	gamma-rays, ultraviolet	N. Getoff	1966	62
Hydrocarbons					
arenes and small am't aliphatics; even number C-atoms mainly	CH_4, NH_3, H_2O through silica gel	1000°C	J. Oro', et al.	1966	63
arenes from 1–4 or more rings; even number C-atoms mainly	CH_4 through silica gel	1000°C	J. Oro', et al.	1966	63
homogeneous mixture of aliphatics, mono-polycyclic compds.	CH_4	semicorona spark	C. Ponnamperuma, et al.	1966	64
Porphyrins					
tetraphenylporphin	pyrrole, benzaldehyde	spontaneous	A. Szutka, et al.	1965	65

[a] AR = adenosine and ribose; ADP = adenosine diphosphate; A4P = adenosine tetraphosphate; GMP = guanosine monophosphate; CMP = cytidine monophosphate; UMP = uridine monophosphate; TMP = thymidine monophosphate; EtMtP = ethylmetaphosphate; PPA = polyphosphoric acid; PPE = polyphosphoric ester.

a lively exchange, sometimes acrimonious, continues to take place. Now no introductory biology book is complete without some mention of the problem.

It might be supposed that the most difficult hurdle has been overcome: It has been unequivocally demonstrated that all kinds of organic compounds, many of them found in living things today, could have been formed abiotically under a variety of conditions. But, with this obstacle removed, the remaining hurdles still appear formidable. For example, how does a living thing come about from a homogeneous "soup" of organic compounds? Some answers to this question are considered in the next chapter.

References

1. S. L. Miller, *Science* **117**, 528 (1953).
2. _____, *J. Am. Chem. Soc.* **77**, 2351 (1955).
3. K. Bahadur, *Nature* **173**, 1141 (1954).
4. S. W. Fox, J. E. Johnson, and M. Middlebrook, *J. Am. Chem. Soc.* **77**, 1048 (1955).
5. P. H. Abelson, *Carnegie Inst. of Wash. Yearbook* **55**, 171 (1956).
6. _____, *Carnegie Inst. of Wash. Yearbook* **56**, 179 (1956).
7. M. L. Hough and A. F. Rogers, *J. Physiol.* **132**, 28 P (1956).
8. T. Hasselstrom, M. C. Henry, and B. Murr, *Science* **125**, 350 (1957).
9. K. Heyns, W. Walter, and E. Meyer, *Naturwissenschaften* **44**, 385 (1957).
10. K. Bahadur, S. Ranganayaki, L. Santamaria, *Nature* **182**, 1668 (1958).
11. J. Oro', A. Kimball, R. Fritz, and F. Master, *Arch. Biochem. Biophys.* **85**, 115 (1959).
12. T. E. Pavlovskaya and A. G. Pasynskii in A. I. Oparin, (ed.), "The Origin of Life on the Earth," *I. U. B. Sympos. Series Vol. 1* Pergamon Press, New York, 1959, p. 151.
13. J. Oro' and J. S. Kamat, *Nature* **190**, 442 (1961).
14. G. Ferrari and R. Cultera, *Nature* **190**, 326 (1961).

15. S. W. Fox and K. Harada, *Science* **133,** 1923 (1961).
16. J. Oro', *Ann. N.Y. Acad. Sci.* **108,** 464 (1963).
17. C. U. Lowe, M. W. Rees, and R. Markham, *Nature* **199,** 219 (1963).
18. K. Harada and S. W. Fox, in "The Origins of Prebiol. Systems," S. W. Fox (ed.), Academic Press, New York, 1965, p. 187.
19. K. A. Grossenbacher and C. A. Knight in *ibid,* p. 173.
20. R. A. Sanchez, J. P. Ferris, and L. E. Orgel, *Science* **154,** 784 (1966).
21. J. P. Ferris and L. E. Orgel, *J. Am. Chem. Soc.* **87,** 4976 (1965).
22. A. S. Chougal and R. M. Lemmon, *Nature* **210,** 628 (1966).
23. J. Oro', *Nature* **190,** 389 (1961).
24. F. Woeller and C. Ponnamperuma, *Abstract of Paper for Joint Meeting of Optical Soc. of Amer., Amer. Chem. Soc. for Applied Spectroscopy,* San Francisco, Calif. 1966.
25. R. R. Becker and A. M. Stahmann, *J. Biol. Chem.* **204,** 737 (1953).
26. H. Hanafusa and S. Akabori, *Bull. Chem. Soc. Japan* **32,** 626 **(1959).**
27. G. Steinman, R. M. Lemmon, and M. Calvin, *Proc. Natl. Acad. Sci.* **52,** 27 (1964).
28. G. Steinman, D. H. Kenyon, and M. Calvin, *Nature* **206,** 707 (1965).
29. C. Ponnamperuma and E. Peterson, *Science* **147,** 1572 (1965).
30. G. Steinman, R. M. Lemmon, and M. Calvin, *Science* **147,** 1574 (1965).
31. G. Schramm and H. Wissmann, *Chem. Ber.* **91,** 1073 (1958).
32. G. Schramm, H. Grötsch, and W. Pollmann, *Angew. Chem. Intern. Ed. Engl.* **1,** 1 (1962).
33. S. W. Fox and K. Harada, *Science* **128,** 1214 (1958).
34. S. W. Fox, T. Waehneldt, C. R. Windsor, and J. Ryan, *2nd Annual Report of the Institute Molec. Evol. Univ. of Miami,* Coral Gables, Florida, 1966.
35. C. Ponnamperuma and J. Flores, *Abstract of Paper for 152nd Natl. Meeting Am. Chem. Soc.* **1,** New York, N.Y., 1966.
36. C. Ponnamperuma, *Abstracts, Third Int. Congress of Radiation Res.,* Cortina D'Ampezzo, 1966.

37. C. Ponnamperuma and R. Mack, *Science* **148**, 1221 (1965).

38. C. Ponnamperuma and P. Kirk, *Nature* **203**, 400 (1964).

39. C. Ponnamperuma, C. Sagan, and R. Mariner, *Nature* **199**, 222 (1963).

40. C. Ponnamperuma, R. S. Young, and E. Munoz, *Fed. Proc.* **22**, 479 (1963).

41. C. Ponnamperuma and R. Mariner, *19th Intern. Congr. Pure Appl. Chem.*, London (1963).

42. C. Ponnamperuma, R. M. Lemmon, R. Mariner, and M. Calvin, *Proc. Natl. Acad. Sci.* **49**, 737 (1963).

43. J. Oro', *Biochem. Biophys. Res. Commun.* **2**, 407 (1960).

44. J. Oro' and A. P. Kimball, *Arch. Biochem. Biophys.* **94**, 217 (1961).

45. C. Ponnamperuma and R. Mack, *Abstract of Paper for 150th Natl. Meeting Am. Chem. Soc.*, Atlantic City, N.J., 1965.

46. C. Ponnamperuma, in "The Origins of Prebiol. Systems," S. W. Fox (ed.), Academic Press, N.Y., 1965, p. 221.

47. N. K. Kochetkov, E. I. Budowsky, V. D. Domkin, and N. N. Kromov-Borissov, *Biochim. Biophys. Acta* **80**, 145 (1964).

48. A. W. Schwartz, E. Bradley, and S. W. Fox, in "The Origins of Prebiol. Systems," S. W. Fox (ed.), Academic Press, N.Y., 1965, p. 317.

49. G. Schramm, personal communication, 1966.

50. R. Berger, *Proc. Natl. Acad. Sci.* **47**, 1434 (1961).

51. C. Palm and M. Calvin, *J. Am. Chem. Soc.* **84**, 2115 (1962).

52. J. Oro' and C. C. Guidry, *Nature* **186**, 156 (1960).

53. J. Oro' and A. C. Cox, *Federation Proc.* **21**, 80 (1962).

54. P. T. Mora in "The Origins of Prebiol. Systems," S. W. Fox (ed.), Academic Press, N.Y. 1965, p. 281.

55. W. A. Allen and C. Ponnamperuma, personal communication, 1966.

56. W. M. Garrison, D. C. Morrison, J. G. Hamilton, A. A. Benson, and M. Calvin, *Science* **114**, 416 (1951).

57. I. E. Elpiner and A. V. Sokolskaya in I. U. B. Sympos. Series Vol. *1*, 1959, p. 172.

58. T. Waldsten and S. Anderson, *Acta Chim. Scand.* **13**, 1069 (1959).

59. C. Sagan and S. L. Miller, *Astronomy J.* **65**, 499 (1960).

60. S. L. Miller and M. Parris, *Nature* **204,** 1248 (1964).
61. A. Schimpel, R. M. Lemmon, and M. Calvin, *Science* **147,** 149 (1965).
62. N. Getoff, *Nature* **210,** 940 (1966).
63. J. Oro' and H. Han, *Science* **153,** 1393 (1966).
64. C. Ponnamperuma and K. Pering, *Nature* **209,** 979 (1966).
65. A. Szutka and R. H. Radzilowski, *Zeit. Naturforschung* **20 b,** 217 (1961).
66. S. L. Miller and H. C. Urey, *Science* **130,** 245 (1959).
67. H. C. Urey, "The Planets," Yale University Press, New Haven, Conn. 1952.

chapter five

The Origin of the First Living Things

The term prebiological system is used to describe microscopic multimolecular droplets that conceivably could have been the starting point for the development of primitive cells. The separation of microscopic droplets from complex macromolecular solutions appears to take place readily under a variety of conditions. Oparin[1] featured the formation of coacervates from colloidal solutions in his explanation of the origin of life. Fox[2,3] and his co-workers have proposed proteinoid microspheres as the basis of the origin of the first primitive cells. Smith[4,5] reported both coacervates and microspheres. Bahadur[6] and his group have snythesized microsphere-like structures which they term "Jeewanu." Chang[7] succeeded in forming microcapsules of synthetic polymers. All of these microstructures have membranes composed of the macromolecules from the medium. They may incorporate in their interior not only some of the same macromolecules but also other substances which may be found in the medium or which may have been introduced into the medium. Each of the types of microstructures will be considered briefly.

COACERVATES

Coacervation was described by Bungenberg de Jong,[8] who experimented with this phenomenon for many years. A solution containing organic macromolecules may undergo coacervation (spontaneous separation into two phases) under proper conditions of temperature, ionic composition and strength, and pH. One phase consists of microscopic droplets (coacervate droplets) high in concentration of macromolecules, and the other is a continuous liquid phase (the equilibrium liquid), relatively impoverished of macromolecules. Coacervation may take place from solutions in which the concentration of macromolecules is as low as one-hundredth per cent. Macromolecules may be concentrated as much as thirty-fold in the resulting coacervate droplets. A medium containing more than one type of macromolecule may yield complex coacervates. From appropriate complex media coacervates possessing an internal organization may separate.

Oparin believed that only in discrete particles could the random chemical activity occurring in the waters of the earth, be organized into harmoniously correlated chemical reactions.[9] This, he felt, would be impossible where reactants were free to mix and drift in all directions. He adapted coacervates to this concept by supposing that in different individual coacervates different groups of reactants could become confined. In this way a wide variety of droplets could be postulated relative to chemical characteristics. Oparin was successful in producing various types of coacervates (Figs. 5-1, 5-2, 5-3). From the same solution, different coacervate droplets concentrated the components of the medium to different extents. He and his co-workers demonstrated the selective concentration in coacervate droplets of various dyes and amino acids. Different amino acids were concentrated in different amounts. Within the same droplet a given component might be unequally distributed. This was especially true of the distribution of nucleic acids. Sugars and mononucleotides seemed to be distributed equally between the medium and the droplets.

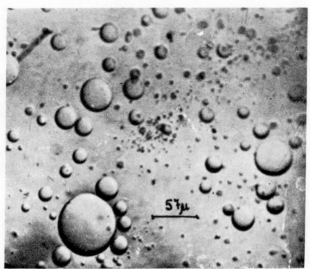

Fig. 5-1. Coacervate droplets of gelatin and gum arabic. From A. I. Oparin, "The Chemical Origin of Life," Charles C. Thomas, Springfield, Ill., 1964, Fig. 8, p 46.

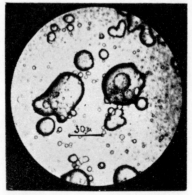

Fig. 5.2. Coacervative droplet having composition of gelatin, gum arabic, and RNA. From A. I. Oparin, "The Chemical Origin of Life," Charles C. Thomas, Springfield, Ill., 1964, Fig. 11c, p 49.

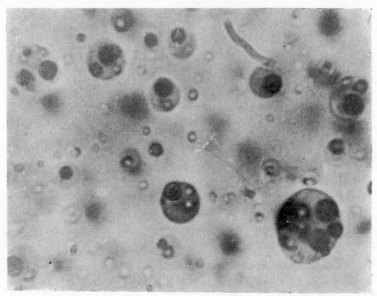

Fig. 5-3. Coacervate droplet containing chlorophyll. From A. I. Oparin, "The Chemical Origin of Life," Charles C. Thomas, Springfield, Ill., 1964, Fig. 15, p 63.

Eventually, a static equilibrium will be established between the medium and the coacervate droplets, and there will be no further exchange between the two. In cells there is a constant influx of materials which enter into the metabolic reactions and a constant outflow of end products. In his recent experiments on coacervate droplets, Oparin has been able to produce a similar effect on a small scale involving one or two chains of reactions. He prepared chlorophyll-containing coacervates, impermeable to the enclosed chlorophyll (Chl), and suspended them in a medium containing reduced ascorbic acid (AcH_2) and oxidized methylene red (MR). In the presence of light ($h\nu$) to activate the chlorophyll (Chl*), a steady-state open system was established by the constant influx of reduced ascorbic acid and oxidized methylene red on the one hand, and the constant outflow of oxidized ascorbic acid (Ac) and reduced methylene red (MRH_2) on the other:

$$
\begin{array}{c}
h\nu \qquad\qquad AcH_2 \quad Ac \qquad\qquad MR \quad MRH_2 \\
\downarrow \qquad\qquad\quad \uparrow \qquad \downarrow \qquad\qquad\quad \downarrow \quad \uparrow \\
\hline
Chl \rightarrow Chl^* \quad \downarrow \qquad \uparrow \qquad ChlH_2 + MR \rightarrow MRH_2 + Chl \\
Chl^* + AcH_2 \rightarrow Ac + ChlH_2
\end{array}
$$

This is an example of the experiments Oparin has conducted in support of his general theory on the origin of cells from a chemical medium. But this is just a beginning and more needs to be done, for the theory goes on to detail the increasing complexity of coacervate chemistry to the level of self-replicating units, for which there is, as yet, no experimental support.

One of the striking things about reactions in microdroplets is that reaction rates for the same reactions are different within the droplet from those in the medium. Fox has reported a similar effect for microspheres.

MICROSPHERES

The microspheres reported by Fox are readily formed from a hot aqueous solution of proteinoid on cooling, when an enormous number of microscopic spherules separates spontaneously from the solution and becomes suspended in it (Fig. 5-4). Fox estimates that 1 gram of proteinoid will yield 10^{10} microspheres. The manner of preparation determines microsphere size (0.5–80 μ) and internal organization (Fig. 5-5).

Fox reports many properties common to cells and microspheres. They show osmotic phenomena, shrinking in hypertonic solutions, and swelling in hypotonic ones. Individual

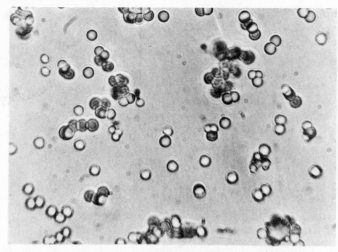

Fig. 5-4. Microspheres Produced from Thermal Proteinoid. Microspheres of uniform size under low magnification. Courtesy S. W. Fox, Institute of Molecular Evolution, University of Miami, Coral Gables, Fla.

microspheres may bud, as do yeasts; some microspheres undergo septate division. A wall can be seen dividing a single unit into two (see arrows in Fig. 5-4). In some cases the daughter units separate entirely and in concentrated protenoid solutions may grow in size and form buds.[14] Microspheres can be readily induced to aggregate into groups. They may aggregate linearly to form filaments as in some bacteria. Microspheres can be prepared having an internal granular organization and an outer boundary, not unlike the simplest bacteria. Increasing the pH of the medium produces microspheres in which the outer boundary is double-layered. Particles within a stationary microsphere have been seen to rotate, a phenomenon which has been interpreted as a primitive form of cytoplasmic streaming. Asymmetric microspheres made from zinc protenoid in a suspension

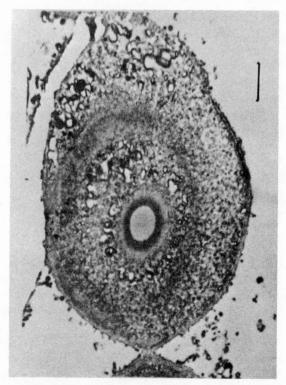

Fig. 5-5. Vacuolar Contents are Shown in Electron Micrograph Produced from Thermal Proteinoid. Courtesy S. W. Fox.

which contains ATP will race around in a nonrandom fashion. Ordinarily, the spherical microspheres show only Brownian movement. Zinc proteinoid has a mild catalytic activity in a number of reactions.[10-13]

Proteinoid microsphere formation has also been reported by Grossenbacher and Knight,[15] and by Young.[16] The latter author has verified many of the observations of Fox. Young

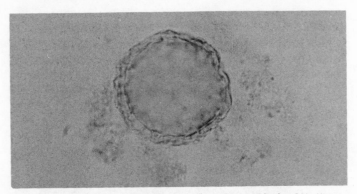

Fig. 5-6. "Blastula-like" Microsphere Made from Proteinoid plus 1% Histone. Courtesy R. S. Young, "Origins of Prebiological Systems," Academic Press, New York, 1965. S. W. Fox (ed.).

has also obtained "blastula-like" microspheres (Fig. 5-6) by the addition of 1 per cent histone to the acidic proteinoid.

Smith,[17] too, has reported the formation of microspheres. By permitting a suspension of microspheres (average diameter 2 μ) to dry in air on a slide and then rehydrating the dried matrix with a drop or two of buffer at pH 8.0, he obtained larger spheres ranging in diameter from 10 to 30 μ (Fig. 5-7). Smith believes that these rehydration spheres resemble the complex coacervates of Oparin. He has also formed coacervates from yeast nucleic acid by the dehydration-rehydration technique.[18] The spheres are relatively large (30–100 μ) and, at the time of formation, show a vigorous internal streaming.

Bahadur and his co-workers have described the formation of a variety of microstructures which they claim exhibit properties of a biological order. They have named these structures Jeewanu (Sanskrit for "particles of life"). An appropriate mixture of chemicals is exposed to sunlight (in some cases to the light of a 500 Watt electric bulb) for a period of time, after which there is generally found a number

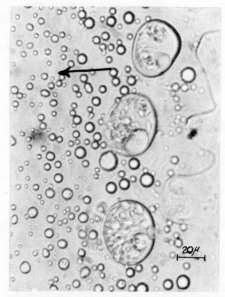

Fig. 5-7. Coacervates Entering the Rehydrant after Budding from the Matrix. Arrow shows direction of coacervate movement.

of microscopic circular objects. Similar solutions, kept in the dark, show none.[19, 20]

Chang's microcapsules,[7] on the other hand, are not intended to represent possible prebiological structures. They are included here to emphasize the ease with which spherical microstructures can be constructed. Chang's aim was to encapsulate microquantities of enzymes in membranes permeable to the substrate of the enzyme but not to the enzyme itself. The encapsulated enzyme can thus escape in vivo degradation and excretion for longer periods while its catalytic function continues at a rate practically as high as the free enzyme.

Probably many more methods could be devised for the

formation of microstructures that could pass for possible precursors to cells in the early history of the earth. Theories on the origin of life, which postulate the gradual development of increasingly more complex chemical systems within microstructures, have a number of models from which to choose.

There is, however, an alternative theory, strongly supported by some authors, which holds that life started as a properly coded nucleic acid—sometimes referred to as the "naked gene" or as the "living macromolecule" theory of the origin of life. The possibility of the abiotic formation of nucleotides and nucleic acids has been established experimentally (see Chapter 4). The nucleic acids thus formed are random polynucleotides of relatively low molecular weight and carry no codes. The naked gene theory explains simply that, given enough time, the random process of polymerization of nucleotides will eventually produce a polynucleotide of the proper sequence to code for its replication, to permit occasional errors of replication, and to bring about the catalysis of other reactions. With these minimum properties of living systems, the naked gene would surround itself with proteins and other substances and thus accumulate a primordial cytoplasm to subserve the nucleic acid. This view would affirm the concept that, in the origin of life, the nucleus came first, while the prebiological systems concept would put the cytoplasm first. These questions will be dealt with more thoroughly in Chapter 8.

References

1. A. I. Oparin, "The Origin of Life on Earth," Macmillan, New York, 1938.
2. S. W. Fox, K. Harada, J. Kendrick, *Science* **129,** 1221 (1959).
3. S. W. Fox, *Paris Colloquium on Elementary Biological Systems and Abiogenesis* (1965).
4. A. E. Smith and F. T. Bellware, *Science* **152,** 362 (1966).
5. A. E. Smith, Personal Communication, 1966.

6. K. Bahadur, *Zbl. Bakt.* **118 II,** 671 (1964).
7. T. M. S. Chang, *Science* **146,** 524 (1964).
8. see A. I. Oparin, in "The Origin of Life on the Earth," Academic Press, New York, 1957, pp. 301–341 ff., for comprehensive discussion of coacervates in relation to the origin of life.
9. A. I. Oparin, "The Chemical Origin of Life," Charles C. Thomas, Springfield, Ill. 1964.
10. G. Krampitz and H. Hardebeck, *Naturwissenschaften* **53,** 81 (1966).
11. S. W. Fox and G. Krampitz, *Nature* **203,** 1362 (1964).
12. D. L. Rohlfing, "Catalytic Activity and Heat Inactivation of Thermal Poly-α-amino Acids," Ph.D. dissertation, Florida State Univ., Tallahassee, Fla. (1964).
13. S. W. Fox, personal communication.
14. _____, personal communication.
15. K. A. Grossenbacher and C. A. Knight, in "The Origins of Prebiological Systems, S. W. Fox (ed.), Academic Press, New York, 1965, p. 173.
16. R. S. Young, in "The Origins of Prebiological Systems," S. W. Fox (ed.), Academic Press, New York, 1963, p. 347.
17. A. E. Smith, personal communication, 1966.
18. _____, personal communication, 1966.
19. O. N. Perti., Agra University Extension Lectures, Agra Univ., Agra, India, 1965, pp. 79, 80.
20. Ibid, p. 86.

chapter six

The Primitive Atmosphere and the Energy Factor

The composition of the primitive atmosphere is fundamental to any theory on the chemical origin of life. Organic compounds that are derived from the simple gases by one mechanism or another furnish the starting point for the origination of the first living things. All workers in this field are agreed that the abiotic formation of organic compounds preceded the origin of life. But there is no general agreement on the constitution of the primitive atmosphere nor on the mechanisms of synthesis of organic compounds.

THE SECONDARY ATMOSPHERE

Most likely, the primitive atmosphere was a secondary one, the original atmosphere having escaped during the formation of the earth.[1-5] The cloud of dust and gas of the future earth began to condense by the agglomeration of dust particles. Before the protoplanet was massive enough to hold an atmosphere, free gases and volatiles escaped. Some of the gases and volatiles were trapped in the accumulating rubble. Others remained behind as nonvolatile compounds, e.g., carbon dioxide as carbonates. Eventually the earth grew sufficiently massive to retain an atmosphere. A hydrosphere and the secondary atmosphere accumulated gradually during geologic time by the escape of volatile substances from rocks that rose more or less continuously from the interior of the earth.

Sagan[6] submitted the question of escape and accumulation of planetary atmospheres to rigorous examination. He confirmed the hypothesis that the original atmosphere of the earth was of a reducing nature, however, it was lost to space before the planet was fully formed. This is further brought out by the fact that the noble gases are considerably less abundant in the atmosphere than in the universe at large. A secondary atmosphere was formed by the outgassing of trapped and combined volatiles from the interior of the earth. There appears, moreover, to have been a further depletion of the noble gases in a differential manner so that those gases of smaller mass were lost to a greater extent.

THE COMPOSITION OF THE ATMOSPHERE

The assumption of a reducing atmosphere advanced by Oparin[7] and by Urey[4] continues to be favored but is facing increasing and more emphatic challenges from various quarters. A reducing atmosphere, as it relates to the problem at hand, consists of a mixture of gases in which the hydrides of the elements are stabilized (C—H, N—H, S—H, O—H, etc.) rather than the oxides (C—O, N—O, S—O, O—O, etc.). In its extreme form such a reducing atmosphere would be composed of CH_4, NH_3, H_2S, H_2O, and H_2. According to Urey[5] the outgassed volatiles were mostly methane, ammonia, water, hydrogen, nitrogen, and some carbon monoxide and carbon dioxide. Miller and Urey[8] analyzed the thermodynamics of an equilibrium mixture of gases in the presence of partial pressures of hydrogen as low as 10^{-4} Atm. and came to the conclusion that it is valid to postulate a primitive reducing atmosphere containing these compounds.

The contention that, with suitable energy, such a mixture of gases would give rise to a great variety and quantity of organic compounds—including biologically important ones —was amply supported by the experiments of Miller.[9,10]

Many subsequent experiments by many different researchers further emphasized this view (Chapter 4). Organic compounds could also be synthesized from gases which were not in their extreme state of reduction. For example, carbon monoxide could be substituted for methane, and nitrogen for ammonia.[11] As long as hydrogen is present or can be generated in sufficient quantity during the course of reactions, even carbon dioxide can substitute for methane. It must be born in mind that a highly energetic source (e.g., ionizing radiation) can produce organic compounds from an oxidizing medium (e.g., $H_2O + CO_2$ (or HCO_3^-)[12,13] although the yield and complexity of compounds is of a low order.

Rubey[3] maintained that an Oparin-Urey type of atmosphere was contradicted by the geologic evidence. Rather, he believed, the main volatiles that resulted from the outgassing process were carbon dioxide, nitrogen, and water with lesser amounts of carbon monoxide and hydrogen. This view has many supporters, among them Holland,[14] Berkner and Marhsall,[15,16] and Abelson.[17] The latter is one of the severest critics of the reducing atmosphere hypothesis. He maintains that a primitive reducing atmosphere would leave evidences of its presence in various ways. For one, irradiation of a reducing mixture of gases containing methane produces hydrophobic organic compounds which are adsorbed by sedimenting clays. The earliest rocks, Abelson states, should therefore contain an unusually large proportion of carbon or organic compounds, but such is not the case. Another argument against the methane-ammonia atmosphere is the instability of ammonia which would be readily degraded under ultraviolet radiation in prebiologic times, at a rate, Abelson asserts, above its rate of re-formation. He thus argues against two of the most important compounds of the postulated reducing atmosphere.

Abelson states that the substances brought into the atmosphere by outgassing were carbon dioxide, carbon monoxide, water, nitrogen, and hydrogen. Water condensed and formed alkaline seas of pH between 8 and 9. Carbon dioxide dissolved in these waters and formed carbonates. Carbon monoxide was converted to formic acid and formate. Some of the carbon dioxide would be reduced by hydrogen and ultraviolet radiation (especially at the elevated temperatures at the top of the atmosphere) into carbon monoxide. Nitrogen would continue to accumulate as it formed and the evidence is that from a relatively low concentration in prebiologic times it has gradually attained its present concentration in the atmosphere.

Holland[14] arrives at the conclusion that volcanic gases in the early atmosphere were highly reducing, and methane and ammonia were probably present. He estimates that this period lasted for the first 500 million years or less, after which the ejected gases were of a less reducing character and contained predominantly carbon dioxide and nitrogen. This second state, in which very little or no free oxygen was present, lasted about 3 billion years (i.e., up to about 1 billion years ago). Then oxygen began to accumulate, mainly as a result of photosynthesis.

The lighter components—hydrogen, ammonia, and methane—must have escaped more readily from the outgassed atmosphere than the heavier carbon dioxide. Thus, even the secondary atmosphere would become less and less reducing in time from this cause alone. Photolysis of water would produce hydrogen and oxygen. The loss of the hydrogen from the atmosphere and the combination of the oxygen with reduced substances in the atmosphere and the crust would contribute further to the decrease in reducing conditions.

THE ENERGY FACTOR

Many forms of energy have been used in experiments on the abiotic synthesis of organic compounds (see Table 4-2), which can be summarized as follows:

Radiation: gamma rays, x-rays, ultraviolet rays, light, heat (infrared rays)

Electricity: sparking, silent discharge

High-energy Particles: alpha-particles, beta-particles

Ultrasonics

Hypersonics

Most of the syntheses were uncatalyzed. However, a limited number of catalysts has been used in some experiments. These were mainly iron and molybdenum compounds, and various phosphates from orthophosphoric acid or its salts to complex metaphosphate esters.

Cosmic and solar radiation and the decay of radioelements have bombarded the earth with energetic rays and particles from the very beginning. The contribution of radioactive decay and cosmic rays to the energy pool was probably not large. Although radioactivity was much greater (2–3.5 times) in the past, the position of radioelements in the lithosphere, many of them at great depths, made radioactivity less effective than other sources for energizing reactions in the atmosphere.

Ionizing radiation has been used by various investigators in the abiotic synthesis of organic compounds under primitive earth conditions. Probably the first to do so was Calvin and his group.[12] They used alpha-particles at 40 Mev from a 60-inch cyclotron with a solution of carbon dioxide as a target and succeeded in synthesizing formic acid and formaldehyde. Miller and Urey[8] felt that the output, in terms of energy expended, was trifling and wrote of it in these words: "This experiment is important in that it induced a reexamination of Oparin's hypothesis of a reducing atmosphere." Be that as it may, ionizing radiation has been used successfully in many syntheses (Table 4-2).

A further criticism by Miller and Urey was based on the

observation that ionizing radiation represents only a small fraction of the earth's available energy (Table 6-1). Ultraviolet radiation does comprise the major source of energy available for prebiotic synthesis of organic compounds; however, this form of energy is more difficult than electric sparking to apply and control in experiments. In addition, electric discharges produce parts of the electromagnetic spectrum, create strong electric fields and generate heat in which ionization of gases can take place. Moreover, the energized particles may, in turn, emit energy in characteristic wavelengths which can serve as a secondary activating source for other atoms and molecules. This complexity may be the basis for the greater efficacy of electric discharges over other forms of energy in the experiments on the production of organic compounds under presumed primitive earth conditions. Miller, in his 1953 and subsequent experiments, used silent discharges and electric sparking.

TABLE 6-1.   Present Sources of Energy Averaged Over the Earth.

Source	Energy $(cal\ cm^{-2}\ yr^{-1})$
Total radiation from sun	260,000
Ultraviolet light	
$\lambda < 2500$ A	570
$\lambda < 2000$ A	85
$\lambda < 1500$ A	3.5*
Electric discharges	4 †
Cosmic rays	0.0015
Radioactivity (to 1.0 km depth)	0.8‡
Volcanoes	0.13§

*Includes the 1.9 cal cm^{-2} yr^{-1} from the Lyman a at 1216 A (*39*). †Includes 0.9 cal cm^{-2} yr^{-1} from lightning and about 3 cal cm^{-2} yr^{-1} due to corona discharges from pointed objects (*40*). ‡The value, 4×10^9 years ago, was 2.8 cal cm^{-2} yr^{-1} (*41*). §Calculated on the assumption of an emission of lava of 1 km^3 (C_p = 0.25 cal/g, P = 3.0 g/cm^3) per year at 1000°C. From S. L. Miller and H. C. Urey, *Science* **130**, 245 (1959).

Heat, as a source of energy for syntheses, has been used primarily by Fox and by Oro' and at times by others (Schramm, Lowe et al., Mora, and Ponnamperuma; see Table 4-2). The objections raised against the use of heat— that its occurrence was and is local and unpredictable, that its total contribution to the energy pool is small, and that it produces tars, not useful products, when amino acids are heated together—have been contested by Fox.[18,19] He has shown that under certain conditions, possible on the primitive earth, amino acids polymerize into long-chain polypeptides instead of tars, that local cycles of high heat and subsequent cooling are the very conditions necessary for polymer and microsphere production, and, he further argues, that long periods of time were not necessarily prerequisite either to the synthesis of organic compounds or to the formation of prebiological systems. This seems indeed to be the case in the context of the "proteinoid" microspheres which he has been able to produce, but although he has won supporters to his concept of prebiological systems, his hypothesis has not yet received widespread acceptance.

Bright sunlight and light from a 500 Watt lamp was used by Bahadur in synthesizing amino acids from *para*-formaldehyde, nitrates, and inorganic catalysts under atmospheric conditions. Nitrates must be reduced to the level of ammonia, and *para*-formaldehyde must yield carbon-carbon bonds. The energy barrier in such reactions, especially in the presence of atmospheric oxygen, would appear to be too great to be overcome by light. Santamaria and Fleishmann[20] reported a confirmation of the work of Bahadur and extended the list of effective catalysts to include $CuSO_4$, $FeCl_3$, $NiCO_3$, and $CoCl_2$.

Ultrasonic vibrations have also been suggested as an energy source in the activation of reactants.[21] Exposure of a mixture of nitrogen and hydrogen in distilled water to ultrasonic vibrations yielded measurable amounts of ammonia. Distilled water, carbon monoxide, hydrogen and nitrogen, under the same conditions, gave measurable amounts of formaldehyde. These findings cannot be properly evaluated because the quantity of ultrasonic vibrations at the time in question is an unknown factor.

A recent addition to this array of energies is hypersonics. Hochstim[22] has calculated the effect of the entrance of meteorites into the atmosphere (Fig. 6-1) and has come up with some surprising and impressive figures. A meteorite with a radius of 500 meters and a velocity of 11 km/sec will have 400,000 tons of gas in its stagnation region, compressed to 1500 Atm. pressure, and will create a temperature of 16,300°K. Its kinetic energy will be equivalent to 40,000 megatons of TNT! The chemical reactivity engendered by this is equally impressive and will be mentioned in the next chapter.

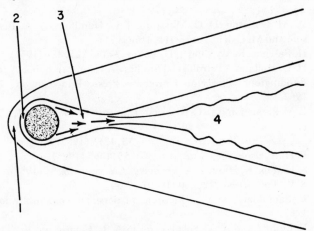

Fig. 6-1. *Hypersonic Flow Around Meteorite. (1) Stagnation region. (2) Boundary layer. (3) Ablating (evaporating) species. (4) Inner wake. From A. R. Hochstim, Proc. Natl. Acad. Sci.* **50**, *200 (1963).*

References

1. W. W. Rubey, *Geol. Soc. Am. Bull.* **62,** 1111 (1951).
2. F. R. Moulton, *Astrophys. J.* **22,** 165 (1905).
3. W. W. Rubey, *Geol. Soc. Am. Special Paper* 62 (1955).
4. H. C. Urey, *The Planets,* Yale University Press, New Haven, Conn., 1952.
5. H. C. Urey, "The Atmosphere of the Planets," in *Handbuch der Physik,* S. Flügge (ed.), **52,** Astrophysik III, Das Sonnensystem, pp. 363–418, Springer Verlag, Berlin 1959.
6. C. Sagan, Preprint from Section I of "Origin of the Earth," in *International Dictionary of Geophysics,* S. K. Runcorn (ed.-in-chief), H. C. Urey (section ed.), Pergamon Press, London, 1965.
7. A. I. Oparin. *The Origin of Life on Earth,* Macmillan, New York, 1938.
8. S. L. Miller and H. C. Urey, *Science* **130,** 245 (1959).
9. S. L. Miller, *Science* **117,** 528 (1953).
10. _____, *J. Am. Chem. Soc.* **77,** 2351 (1955).
11. P. H. Abelson, Carnegie Institution of Washington, *Yearbook* **55,** 171 (1955), *Yearbook* **56,** 179 (1956).
12. W. M. Garrison, D. C. Morrison, J. G. Hamilton, A. A. Benson, and M. Calvin, *Science* **114,** 416 (1951).
13. H. Paschke, R. W. Chang, D. Young, *Science* **125,** 881 (1957).
14. H. D. Holland, "Petrological Studies: A volume to honor A. F. Buddington," Princeton University Press, Princeton, N. J., 1962.
15. L. V. Berkner and L. C. Marshal, *Discussion Faraday Soc.* **37,** 122 (1964).
16. _____, *Proc. Natl., Acad. Sci., U.S.* **53,** 1215 (1965).
17. P. H. Abelson, *Proc. Natl., Acad. Sci.* **55,** 1365 (1966).
18. S. W. Fox, K. Harada, A. Vegotsky, *Experientia* **15,** 81 (1959).
19. S. W. Fox, *Science* **132,** 200 (1960).
20. L. Santamaria and L. Fleishmann, personal communication, 1965.
21. E. Elpiner and A. V. Sokolskaya, in A. L. Oparin (ed.), "The Origin of Life on the Earth," (I.U.B. Symposium Series Vol. 1), Pergamon Press, New York, 1959, p. 172.
22. A. R. Hochstim, *Proc. Natl. Acad. Sci.* **50,** 200 (1963).

chapter seven

Reaction Mechanisms

Great interest was shown almost from the start in the chemical mechanisms that could be responsible for the formation of so great a variety of organic and biochemical compounds. It is only natural to seek such mechanisms from among those familiar in organic chemical syntheses or biosyntheses. But some of the suggested pathways represent less an analysis of possible chemical mechanisms than an exercise with paper and pencil. A perspective to keep in mind is the fact that modern biochemical pathways are the result of billions of years of evolution. It is unlikely that anything resembling a biochemical pathway was present or possible among the mixture of chemicals in the proposed "prebiotic soup." With few exceptions, the simulated primitive earth conditions employed by investigators are harsh; not only inimical to present living things, but destructive to polymeric substances. It is possible that the mechanisms involved in the synthesis of organic compounds on the primitive earth were indeed harsh, that the first prebiological structures retained these mechanisms, and that evolution of a milder chemistry took place primarily in these structures.

Miller[1] considered two possible mechanisms: (1) Hydrogen cyanide, aldehydes, nitriles, and amines, and part of the polymers are synthesized in the electric discharge and the amino, hydroxy, and aliphatic acids are formed by hydrolysis of the respective nitriles in the solution. (2) All the products identified are synthesized in the gas phase from radicals and ions formed in the electric discharge. To test these alternatives, Miller followed the change in concentration of products in samples periodically withdrawn from the gas phase and from the liquid phase during the course of the experiment. Fig. 7-1 shows the change in concentration, with time, of ammonia, hydrogen cyanide, and aldehydes in the gas phase,

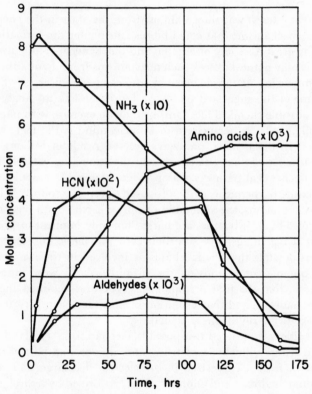

Fig. 7-1. *Concentrations of Ammonia, Hydrogen cyanide, and Aldehydes in the U-tube, and Amino acids in the 500-ml Flask while Sparking a Mixture of Methane, Ammonia, Water, and Hydrogen in the Apparatus of Fig. 4-1. From S. L. Miller, Biochim. Biophys. Acta 23, 484 (1957).*

and of amino acids in the liquid phase. The results would thus seem to favor the first alternative, for which the following mechanisms seem likely:

Hydrogen cyanide is an early product. It may have several origins. Hydrogen cyanide can form directly from the interaction between methane and ammonia:

$$CH_4 + NH_3 \rightarrow HCN + 3H_2$$

Other hydrocarbons, as they form, can also give rise to hydrogen cyanide on reacting with ammonia. Carbon monoxide is still another possible source for hydrogen cyanide:

$$CO + NH_3 \rightarrow HCN + H_2O$$

SYNTHESIS OF ORGANIC COMPOUNDS

In the spark, methane will form carbon-carbon bonds yielding two-carbon compounds, for example, C_2H_2, C_2H_4, C_2H_6. In the presence of hydrogen cyanide, the hydrocarbons yield nitriles:

$$C_2H_4 + HCN \rightarrow CH_3CH_2CN$$
Propionitrile

or
$$C_2H_2 + 2HCN \rightarrow NCCH_2CH_2CN$$
Succinodinitrile

The corresponding acids are obtained when the nitriles are hydrolyzed in the aqueous phase:

$$CH_3CH_2CN + 2H_2O \rightarrow CH_3CH_2COOH + NH_3$$
Propionic acid

$$NCCH_2CH_2CN + 4H_2O \rightarrow HOOCCH_2CH_2COOH + 2NH_3$$
Succinic acid

With hydrogen cyanide, aldehydes form the corresponding hydroxynitriles, which on hydrolysis will yield the hydroxy acids.

$$CH_3CHO + HCN \rightleftharpoons CH_3CHOHCN \xrightarrow{2H_2O}$$
Acetaldehyde

$$CH_3CHOHCOOH + NH_3$$
Lactic Acid

$$CH_3CH_2CHO + HCN \rightleftharpoons CH_3CH_2CHOHCN \xrightarrow{2H_2O}$$
Propionaldehyde

$$CH_3CH_2CHOHCOOH + NH_3$$
α-Hydroxybutyric acid

With ammonia, the hydroxynitriles can form the corresponding aminonitriles from which the amino acids may be obtained by hydrolysis:

$$CH_3CHOHCN \xrightarrow{NH_3} CH_3CHNH_2CN + H_2O$$
$$\downarrow{2H_2O}$$
$$CH_3CHNH_2COOH + NH_3$$
Alanine

$$CH_3CH_2CHOHCN \xrightarrow{NH_3} CH_3CH_2CHNH_2CN + H_2O$$
$$\downarrow{2H_2O}$$
$$CH_3CH_2CHNH_2COOH + NH_3$$
α-Aminobutyric acid

The mechanism of formation of the β-amino acid β-alanine probably follows a different course. Ammonia makes a nucleophilic attack on the β carbon of acrylonitrile or acrylamide, and the resulting compound undergoes hydrolysis to β-alanine:

$$CH_2CHCN \xrightarrow{NH_3} CH_2NH_2CH_2CN \xrightarrow{2H_2O}$$
Acrylonitrile β-Aminopropionitrile

$$CH_2NH_2CH_2COO + NH_3$$
β-Alanine

$$CH_2CHCONH_2 \xrightarrow{NH_3} CH_2\overset{\overset{\displaystyle NH_2}{|}}{CH}\cdots\overset{\overset{\displaystyle NH_2}{|}}{\underset{\underset{\ominus}{\smile}}{C}}\cdots O \xrightarrow{H_2O}$$

Acrylamide

β-Aminopropionamide

$$CH_2NH_2CH_2COO^- + NH_3$$

β-Alanine

The use of heat in simulated prebiological syntheses has revealed some interesting facts. Vacilating temperatures can bring about, in sequence, the synthesis of amino acids, the polymerization of these into protein-like polymers, and the formation from the latter of microscopic structures. Harada and Fox[13] synthesized amino acids simultaneously by passing ammonia, methane, and steam over silica, in a vicor tube heated to ca. 1000°C. Amino acids were synthesized at lower temperatures (ca. 130°C) by heating malic acid with urea or ammonia.[2] At 150°C the amino acids polymerize to form protein-like polypeptides. The ease with which amino acids will polymerize into polypeptides, especially in the presence of an excess of aspartic and glutamic acids, makes it possible to visualize natural conditions under which such events might have taken place. Ammonia, methane, and steam are present in the gases of an active volcano. Temperatures in volcanoes may reach 1000°C and higher. Under these conditions the formation of amino acids is possible. These amino acids can then polymerize into polypeptides on the cooling lava. Rain can dissolve the hot polymers, and the solution, on cooling, can give rise to microspheres. The laboratory experiments of Fox suggest this counterpart in nature.

Ionizing radiation, very high temperature, and electric sparking create high energy species. Under the impact of sufficient energy, compounds become dissociated and give rise to free radicals, neutral species, and ions. The results of the interaction among these can be very complex and practically unpredictable. A good example is the report of Hochstim[16] on "hypersonic chemosynthesis." The high temperature and pressure created by the entry of the meteorite, mentioned in chapter 6, into the atmosphere, will convert the atoms of all compounds present into excited species. The same kinds of ions and free radicals will form, whether the atmosphere contained CO, CO_2, CH_4 (or other hydrocarbon source), NH_3, NO_2, NO (or other nitrogen source), H_2S, SO_2 (or other sulfur source), etc. The energetic species would be C, C^+, O, O^+, e^-, N, N^+, H, H^+, OH, NO, NO^+, S, etc. Behind the meteorite, lower temperatures are encountered, and combinations can take place: N_2, O_2, C_2, H_2, C_3, O_3, C_4, N_2^+, H_2^+, O_2^+, CO, CO_2, CH, CH_2, CH_4, CH^+, CN, CN^+, C_2N_2, NH, NH_2, NO, N_2O, NO_2, NH_3, OH, OH^-, H_2O, HS, H_2S, SO, SO_4, etc. Evaporation from the meteorite would yield Fe, Fe^+, Ni, Ni^+, P, PO, FeO, CuO, FeN, FeC, etc. Impact with water would mix water vapor with the reactive species and would result in formation of simple and complex organic compounds. In preliminary experiments a high velocity bullet was fired through a mixture of CH_4, NH_3, and H_2 into water. The water was found to contain traces of organic compounds.

Recombination of free radicals of carbon will form predominantly branched chain compounds. Oro'[3] suggested the formation of acetylene from carbon radicals as an intermediate in the abiological synthesis of styrene which, in turn, would give rise to the aromatic amino acids phenylalanine and tyrosine.

One of the most interesting mechanisms has to do with the reactions of activated hydrogen cyanide. Hydrogen cyanide appears among the first products of the gases in mixtures used in experiments on the abiological synthesis of organic compounds. This has suggested to many authors that hydrogen cyanide may have played a primary role in primordial organic chemical syntheses. Oro'[4] detected adenine among

the reaction products from a mixture of HCN, NH_3, and
H_2O. This was confirmed in subsequent work, and a probable reaction mechanism was proposed by Oro' and Kimball[5] (Fig. 7-2).

The 4-aminoimidazole-5-carboxamidine (AICAI) formed in
reaction (5) gives rise to 4-aminoimidazole-5-carboxamide
(AICA), which in turn is the starting point for the formation
of the purines guanine, xanthine, and hypoxanthine
(Fig. 7-3).

Kliss and Matthews proposed an interesting hypothesis in
1962[6] (further elaborated by Matthews and Moser in 1966[7]

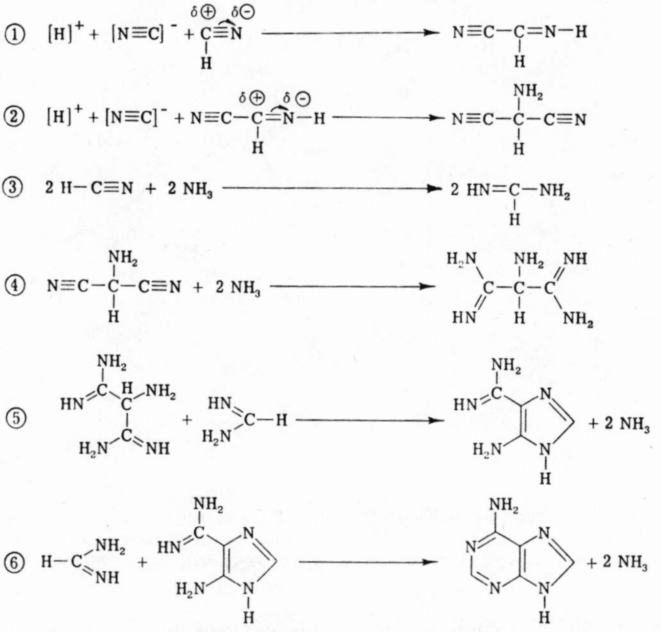

Over-all reaction: 5 HCN = Adenine

Fig. 7-2. *Mechanism of Formation of Adenine from Hydrogen Cyanide.*
From J. Oro' in "The Origin of Prebiological Systems and of their Chemical
Matrices," S. W. Fox (ed.), Academic Press, New York, 1965, p. 153.

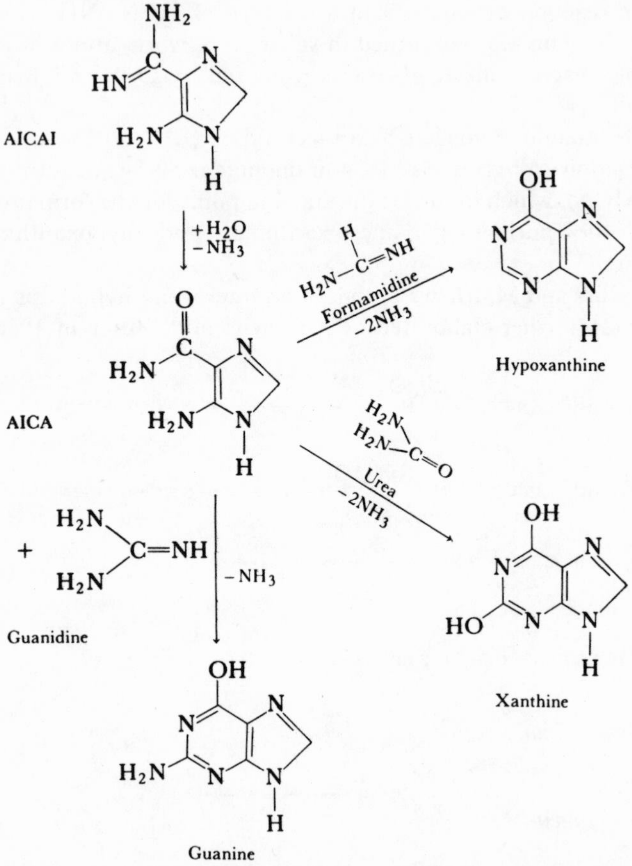

Fig. 7-3. Proposed Mechanism for the Synthesis of Purines on the Primitive Earth. After J. Oro' in "The Origin of Prebiological Systems and of their Chemical Matrices," S. W. Fox (ed.), Academic Press, New York, 1965, p. 152.

and 1967[7a]) in which they suggested the formation of proteins and purines from an active dimer of hydrogen cyanide, aminocyanocarbene, a ground state singlet compound with considerable dipolar character. The formation of the dimer is pictured as follows[7a]:

$$2HCN \rightarrow \underset{HN}{\overset{H}{\diagdown}} C-C\equiv N \xrightarrow{\text{(tautomerization)}} H_2 N \overset{\delta+}{=\!\!=} C \overset{\delta-}{=\!\!=} C \overset{\delta-}{\equiv\!\!\equiv} N$$

aminocyanocarbene
$(HCN)_2$

$(HCN)_2$ rapidly and spontaneously polymerizes into a poly-aminoketenimine which, after tautomerization, reacts further with hydrogen cyanide to yield a polyaminomalononitrile (PAMN). This sequence can be represented:

$$n(HCN)_2 \rightarrow \left(\begin{array}{c} C=C=N \\ | \\ NH_2 \end{array} \right)_n \longrightarrow$$

$$\left(\begin{array}{c} C-C=N \\ \| \\ NH \end{array} \right)_n \xrightarrow{\text{HCN}} \left(\begin{array}{c} \quad CN \\ \quad | \\ C-C-NH \\ \| \; | \\ NH \; H \end{array} \right)_n$$

PAMN

PAMN would tend to adopt alpha-helix structures, both right-handed and left-handed. Side-chain formation for the future protein would begin with PAMN by reaction of the projecting nitrile groups with hydrogen cyanide; interaction of water with various projecting imino and cyano groups followed by decarboxylation would yield peptide structures. This sequence can be represented:

$$\left(\begin{array}{c} \quad CN \\ \quad | \\ C-C-N \\ \| \; | \\ NH \; H \end{array} \right)_n \xrightarrow{\text{HCN}} \left(\begin{array}{c} \quad R' \\ \quad | \\ C-C-NH \\ \| \; | \\ NH \; H \end{array} \right)_n \xrightarrow{H_2O}$$

$$\left(\begin{array}{c} \quad R'' \\ \quad | \\ C-C-NH \\ \| \; | \\ O \; H \end{array} \right)_n \xrightarrow{-CO_2} \left(\begin{array}{c} \quad R \\ \quad | \\ C-C-NH \\ \| \; | \\ O \; H \end{array} \right)_n$$

polypeptide

R represents 15 different alpha-amino acid side chains whose precursors are R' and R''. Other reactions at those sites involve acetylene and hydrogen sulfide, accounting for the aromatic and sulfur-containing side chains.

The 1,3-biradical of the HCN dimer could also react to form purines. The suggested sequence of reactions for adenine synthesis is given as follows:

Adenine

These ideas were tested experimentally. Adenine, diaminomalononitrile, and a black viscous tar were retrieved. On hydrolysis the tar yielded a number of amino acids. Kliss and Matthews also suggested the formation of hexoses and pentoses through the polymerization of HCN.

Akabori[14] had earlier proposed that the first proteins were formed directly from a polyglycine precursor. The latter has the structure

$$\cdots\cdots-\underset{H}{N}-\underset{\underset{O}{\parallel}}{\overset{\overset{CH_2}{|}}{C}}-\underset{H}{N}-\overset{\overset{CH_2}{|}}{\underset{\underset{O}{\parallel}}{C}}\cdots$$

in which one hydrogen of each methylene group (CH_2) would be subject to attack from outside reactants. In this way the various side chains characteristic of a protein can be introduced. The polyglycine itself results from the polymerization of aminoacetonitrile, which forms readily from ammonia, formaldehyde, and hydrogen cyanide:

$$CH_2O + NH_3 + HCN \xrightarrow{\quad H_2O \quad} \underset{\text{Aminoacetonitrile}}{H_2NCH_2CN} \xrightarrow{\quad \text{Polymerization} \quad}$$

$$\left(-NH-CH_2-\underset{\underset{NH}{\parallel}}{C}-\right)_x \xrightarrow[-xNH_3]{+xH_2O} \underset{\text{Polyglycine}}{(-NH-CH_2-CO-)_x}$$

Experimentally,[15] seryl residues were introduced into polyglycine adsorbed on kaolinite by reaction with formaldehyde:

$$-\underset{H}{N}-\underset{\underset{O}{\parallel}}{\overset{\overset{CH_2}{|}}{C}}-\underset{H}{N}\diagdown \xrightarrow{+CH_2O} -\underset{H}{N}-\underset{\underset{O}{\parallel}}{\overset{\overset{CH_2OH}{\overset{|}{\underset{CH}{|}}}}{C}}-\underset{H}{N}\diagdown$$

while reaction with acetaldehyde introduced threonyl residues:

$$-\underset{H}{N}-\underset{\underset{O}{\parallel}}{\overset{\overset{CH_2}{|}}{C}}-\underset{H}{N}\diagdown \xrightarrow{+CH_3CO} -\underset{H}{N}-\underset{\underset{O}{\parallel}}{\overset{\overset{HOC-CH_3}{\overset{|}{\underset{CH}{|}}}}{\overset{H}{}}}C-\underset{H}{N}\diagdown$$

Introduction of leucyl (or isoleucyl) residues was also demonstrated. Plausible mechanisms for the introduction of other residues—including aromatic and heterocyclic ones—were proposed.

The role of HCN is viewed in a somewhat different light by Calvin and his group.[8-11] The question they wished to answer was "How could dehydration condensations take place in dilute aqueous solution?" Dehydration reactions are thermodynamically forbidden in the presence of excess water. The reported effectiveness of carbodiimides in bringing about dehydration condensations led them to try first cyanamide then dicyanamide, both of which promoted peptide formation from amino acids in dilute aqueous solution. Dicyanamide was by far the more effective agent and the mechanism of its action is being studied.

A possible mode of action for cyanamide was proposed by Calvin.[11] It is based on the observation that this compound dimerizes on standing to dicyandiamide, and it is this dimer that is active:

They found that dicyandiamide favors not only peptide bond formation but also phosphate and acetate esters of primary alcohols (e.g., glucose-6-phosphate, glycerol-1-acetate) as well as the formation of pyrophosphate (e.g., ADP from AMP, and pyrophosphoric acid from orthophosphoric acid).

It was pointed out in the previous chapter that geological considerations favor a primitive atmosphere in which CO, CO_2, N_2, and H_2 were the major components and that the seas attained a pH of 8–9. This is the view Abelson[12] takes and asks "What kind of prebiologic chemistry is there that can occur at ordinary temperatures in dilute solutions at pH 8?" Among other mechanisms, Abelson also considers the properties of HCN. At either high or low pH, HCN will not polymerize, but at pH 8–9 the reaction proceeds well and 0.1 M HCN + cyanide will yield polymers in which the tetramer is prominent.

$$
\begin{array}{ccc}
NH_2 & & CN \\
 & \diagdown C \diagup & \\
 & \| & \\
 & \diagup C \diagdown & \\
NH_2 & & CN \\
\end{array}
$$

Hydrolysis of the tetramer will give glycine. Polymers resulting from ultraviolet irradiation of HCN yield on hydrolysis glycine, alanine, serine, aspartic acid, and glutamic acid.

In this chapter some chemical mechanisms have been considered as possible explanations of the abiotic synthesis of organic compounds on the primitive earth. In the next chapter the view will be developed that many organic compounds (but few of biological significance) were formed in the "soup," and that *biochemical* evolution began in microscopic prebiological structures which concomitantly evolved into cells.

References

1. S. L. Miller in *I. U. B. Symp. Series Vol. 1*, Pergamon Press, New York 1959, p. 123.
2. S. W. Fox, *Science* **132**, 200 (1960).
3. J. Oro', *Proc. Lun. Plan. Expl. Collow.* **3**, No. 2, 9 (1963).
4. _____, *Biochem. and Biophys. Res. Communs.* **2**, 407 (1960).
5. J. Oro' and A. P. Kimball, *Arch. Biochem. Biophys.* **96**, 293 (1962).
6. R. M. Kliss and C. N. Matthews, *Proc. Natl. Acad. Sci.* **48**, 1300 (1962).
7. C. N. Matthews and R. E. Moser, *Proc. Natl. Acad. Sci.* **56**, 1087 (1966).
7a. _____, *Nature* **215**, 1230 (1967).
8. A. Schimpel, R. M. Lemmon, and M. Calvin, *Science* **147**, 149 (1965).
9. G. Steinman, R. M. Lemmon, and M. Calvin, *Science* **147**, 1574 (1965).
10. G. Steinman, D. H. Kenyon, and M. Calvin, *Nature* **206**, 707 (1965).
11. M. Calvin, *Proc. Royal Soc. A.*, **288**, 441 (1965).
12. P. H. Abelson, *Proc. Natl. Acad. Sci.* **55**, 1365 (1966).
13. K. Harada and S. W. Fox in "The Origins of Prebiological Systems" Fox (ed.), Academic Press, New York 1965, p. 187.
14. S. Akabori, *Kagaku (Science in Japan)* **25**, 54 (1955).
15. _____, *I. U. B. Symp. Series Vol. 1*, Academic Press, New York, 1959, p. 189.
16. A. R. Hochstim, *Proc. Natl. Acad. Sci. U.S.* **50**, 200 (1963).

chapter eight

Chemical Problems in the Origin of Life

A NEW PERSPECTIVE

Parts of the present explanation of the chemical origin of life need to be reevaluated. The abiotic origin of organic compounds on the primitive earth is accepted as an early step in that explanation. However, the general tendency is to assume that all the biochemicals essential for life appeared before life originated. This assumption makes an explanation of the origin of life so attractively facile and it so nicely fits in with the concept that spontaneous generation occurred at one time even if it does not occur now, that it has seldom been examined critically. On the other hand, an emerging concept on the origin of life is that it is a part of the gradual evolution of matter which takes place throughout the universe. The assumption that an almost complete biochemistry evolved, even to the level of biochemical pathways in the absence of living things, is inconsistent with this view. For if that were so, we would be saying that, while evolution brought about enormous morphological, physiological and psychological developments, biochemistry—the chemistry of living things—changed but little because its fundamental patterns were set before life appeared!

There is yet another difficulty. The first organism, it is claimed, had to hide from the very elements that led to its creation, for it is generally agreed that atmospheric conditions on the primitive earth, especially the high flux of energetic ultraviolet rays, would destroy any form of life. It is therefore assumed that the first living things were restricted to such depths of water as would shield them from harmful rays, there to stay for millions (perhaps hundreds of millions) of years, awaiting proper conditions. This is inconsistent with the view that each new level of organization of matter emerges from a lower level *and is compatible* with the conditions that brought it about.

The assumption most difficult to accept, however, is the claim that out of a structureless "soup" there arose as the first living thing a "primitive anaerobic microorganism." This is inconceivable since the simplest anaerobe has at least dozens of catalyzed reactions harmoniously correlated to each other, and the whole is controlled by a fine coordination. Even if we were to accept the assumption that each of these reactions preexisted in the "soup," the chance assembly of all of them into a functioning unit is inconceivable. There is now every reason to believe that life was an inevitable outcome of the *gradual evolution* of matter and did not have to depend on *improbable accidental occurrences*.

A more likely approach to the problem would assume that morphology, physiology, and biochemistry evolved together. The concept of a biochemistry in the structureless "soup" might have to be abandoned; so, too, concepts of modern organic chemistry. A profound chemical evolution must have been a part of the vast evolution in morphology and physiology. Conversely, the earliest organic chemical syntheses must have followed different mechanisms than the familiar ones of the present. For example, the first prebiological polymers may have been formed in unfamiliar ways. Many workers have reported yellow, orange, red, brown, or black tars which appeared during experiments on abiotic synthesis. Some of these have been partially analyzed and usually, on hydrolysis, they yield some amino acids. In fact, it would

seem that in experiments on the synthesis of organic compounds under simulated primitive earth conditions, the great
concern with' discovering present-day biochemicals is responsible for some promising substances being discarded as
worthless tarry messes, or being dismissed as irrelevant to
the problem of the origin of life.

The outline of an alternate view may be presented at this
point. The core of the thesis is that two different lines of
organic chemistry evolved side by side during most of the
period of chemical evolution; one taking place in the environment and the other in microscopic droplets which had separated out of the environmental medium early in the chemical
history. This early separation was due to the appearance of
polymeric substances, some of which separated out of the
medium as microdroplets (e.g., Oparin's coacervates, or
Fox's microspheres, or the spherules described by Grossenbacher and Knight.[3])

Within these microscopic precellular structures chemical
activity could become more limited and could gradually
evolve along different lines than that in the unrestricted
medium. In the medium, whether primordial oceans, seas,
or tidal pools, indiscriminate mixing of all components would
tend to produce a homogeneity rather than diversity. On the
other hand, the composition of the microscopic droplets
would depend on the local chemical composition of the
medium; so it is to be expected that from the start there
would be some diversity in chemical composition among
these droplets. The further development of droplets would
depend on the original composition of the droplet and the
physical and chemical nature of the immediate environment.
The overall development of these precellular structures into
primitive cells, however, must not be conceived of solely as
a gradual chemical change toward complexity. It is more in
keeping with the foregoing assumptions that after an amount

of internal chemical change from the original conditions, an abrupt change in internal organization or in the structure of the whole microdroplet took place. The new morphology (i.e., the new organization of the chemicals of the droplet) ushered in a new level of chemical activity which, in turn, further increased the difference in chemistry between droplets and the environmental medium.

An important aspect of this interplay between droplets and the medium is the enrichment of the latter by the occasional breakdown of the droplets. At first, the microdroplets were not permanently stabilized structures. Many, if not most, would eventually break down and thus enrich the environment with organic chemicals that could be synthesized only within the droplets. Each successive reformation of microdroplets from the successively enriched medium would result in structures different than those of previous instances. This mechanism would be an additional means of accounting for the postulated qualitative differentiation of microdroplets.

The eventual establishment of a "primitive cell" would require a number of such qualitative changes, each ushering in a new level of chemical activity having both greater complexity and greater coordination. It may be supposed from this line of reasoning that one of the qualitative jumps must have led to the "living state," the stage just previous to it being the last "inanimate" prebiological structure. However, this is an oversimplification for it assumes that we know precisely what life is; as we shall see, this is far from fact.

EVOLUTION OF BIOCHEMISTRY

A few details of this outline are already visible. When amino acids are heated together under specific conditions, copolymerization takes place, and a polypeptide is formed which resembles protein in many ways.[1] But when Harada and Fox[2,3] set out to demonstrate the thermal synthesis of amino acids from methane, ammonia, and water, they obtained a *polymer*, and the 14 amino acids they reported were obtained *after hydrolysis* of the polymer.

This gives an additional perspective to the reported findings of amino acids by others. Amino acids are found in trace amounts, while polymeric substances usually form early and in fair abundance, as judged from most of the experiments. Some of the polymers on hydrolysis yield a variety of amino acids. These polymers might have formed directly by either the Akabori* or the Kliss-Matthews-Moser* method. It will be recalled that in both cases a glycine or a glycine-like repeating unit makes up the backbone of the developing chain.

$$\text{H} \leftarrow$$

The hydrogen $(-\text{NH}-\overset{|}{\underset{\parallel}{\text{C}}}-\text{CH}-)_n$ (Akabori) or the nitrile
$$\text{O}$$

$$\text{CN} \leftarrow$$

group $(-\overset{|}{\underset{\parallel}{\text{C}}}-\text{CH}-\text{NH}-)_n$ (Kliss, Matthews, Moser) pro-
$$\text{NH}$$

jecting from the methylene carbon of the repeating unit is subject to attack by active species giving rise to the various side chains of amino acids.

In this way a polymer of changing character is built up during the course of the experiment. At first the residues are mainly glycine which are then gradually converted to other amino acids; therefore, it would be expected that, on hydrolysis, the amino acid in greatest yield would be glycine. The abundances of the other amino acids would be in accord with the relative ease of formation of the respective side chains. At present there is little information on the mechanism of formation of such side chains. However,

*See previous chapter.

one can guess that $-CH_3$, $-CH_2OH$, $-CHOHCH_3$, $-CH_2COOH$, $-CH_2CH_2COOH$ (the side chains of alanine, serine, threonine, aspartic acid and glutamic acid, respectively) might require simpler mechanisms than some of the other side chains. In partial confirmation, glycine and alanine are by far the most abundant amino acids in evidence whenever the results of polymer hydrolysis are reported.

The experiments of Grossenbacher and Knight[4] illustrate these points. In a modification of the Miller-type apparatus, they sparked a mixture of methane, ammonia, water vapor, and hydrogen for periods ranging from 10 to 30 days. It is noteworthy that they reported "by 48 hours the liquid acquired a straw color which gradually deepened to amber during the runs ..." By this time (48 hours) spherules ranging in size from about 800 Å to 50 Å or less had appeared in the body of the liquid, and increased in number throughout the experiment. These spherules were reported to be composed in part of organic matter which, on acid hydrolysis, yielded substances that chromatographed like amino acids and gave positive ninhydrin reactions.

In contrast, amino acids could be identified only faintly between 24 and 48 hours: "... one or two definite ninhydrin-reactive spots were observed in the glycine-serine-aspartic acid area of the chromatogram and two or three other faint spots. By 100 hours the number of definite ninhydrin-reactive spots had increased to about four and by 200 hours, eight to twelve ..." including some which occupied locations not usually associated with the 20 common amino acids.

These results are consistent with the hypothesis that a polymer containing amino acid residues was formed first and continued to be formed while it gave rise on the one hand to amino acids by hydrolysis, and on the other, to spherules by separation from the fluid. As explained above, the hydrolosis of this polymer would yield a mixture of amino acids in which glycine, alanine, serine, threonine, aspartic acid, and glutamic acid would be expected in greater amounts than some of the other amino acids. Table 8-1 gives the relative abundances of some of the amino acids reported by various investigators.

TABLE 8-1. Relative Abundances of Amino Acids Produced Under Simulated Primitive Earth Conditions

| Amino Acid | Thermal Synthesis | | Spark Synthesis | |
	Fox (1030°C) %	Oro' (1030°C) %[x]	Grossenbacher et al. %[y]	Miller %[z]
Glycine	24.4	61.05	27.1	55.76
Alanine	20.2	36.78	23.7	30.08
Serine	10.0	0.26	23.7	—
Aspartic acid	15.2	0.06	3.4	0.33
Glutamic acid	10.2	0.26	1.7	0.55
Threonine	3.0	0.66	6.8	—
Leucine	4.6	0.13	3.4	—
Isoleucine	2.5	0.06	3.4	—
Proline	2.3	—	—	—
Valine	2.1	—	—	—
Phenylalanine	2.2	0.01	—	—
Tyrosine	2.0	0.01	—	—
Alloisoleucine	1.4	0.06	—	—
Lysine	—	—	6.8	—
Beta-alanine	—	0.66	—	13.28

[x]Recalculated from the results of Oro', "The Origins of Prebiol. Systems," p. 137.
[y]Recalculated from the results of Grossenbacher, *ibid.*, p. 173.
[z]Recalculated from the results of Miller, *J. Am. Chem. Soc.* **77**, 2351 (1955).

When first formed, the microdroplets would exhibit a chemical reactivity very similar to that of the environmental medium (e.g., the Kliss-Matthews-Moser mechanism of organic chemical synthesis, the Calvin dicyandiamide method of peptide formation, or the Akabori scheme of polyglycine synthesis). Other basic mechanisms of organic chemical synthesis not known now might have been a part of the total chemical reactivity of the medium and the microdroplets. We need not assume that either the microdroplets or the polymers were affected adversely by energetic ultraviolet rays. The first polypeptides were stable molecules having only a primary and perhaps a secondary structure—the latter being brought about by the nature of the covalent bonds in the polyglycine backbone. Kliss and Matthews state that this would result in left-handed and right-handed alpha-helices. This example of the capacity for self-organization of matter was mentioned before and is an important factor in the evolution of morphology.

In view of this, it is a highly significant discovery of Fox[5] that when amino acids are permitted to react at random, *there does not take place a random polymerization* leading to an infinite variety of polypeptides (proteinoids) as predicted by theory. Rather, only some half dozen different types are formed again and again. Obviously, the theory must be at fault in assuming that the reactivity of all carboxyl groups and of all amino groups is the same, and therefore all amino acids should have equal chemical affinities in peptide formation. Apparently this is not so. Different amino acids and peptides have specific pK's which determine the most likely combinations. This turns out to be a severely limiting factor and explains the relatively few types of polypeptides obtained in a spontaneously reacting mixture for amino acids.[6] Therefore, each of the great variety of proteins made in cells represents a specific act of synthesis *and requires energy* for that synthesis, proportional to its departure from the observed spontaneous condition. Thus the energy-consuming synthesis of proteins in living things from an amino acid pool may result in an increase in free energy of the system, while the spontaneous formation of polypeptides from a similar pool results in a decrease in free energy of the system. The fundamental requirements of the second law of thermodynamics are thus met, even though the sequence of amino acids in natural proteins may be more random than that in spontaneously formed polypeptides. "Randomness" and "order" have little or no pertinence in this context in relation to the second law.

Many similar conditions must have applied to the early organic chemistry of the primitive earth. The shift toward biochemistry—biochemical compounds and pathways—is most readily understandable as an evolutionary event *within precellular structures*. Biochemical evolutionary changes probably occured in precellular structures concomitantly with morphological changes, and not in the structureless medium.

In brief, then, it is suggested that polymers, especially polypeptides, resulted directly from the reactions among the gases of the primitive atmosphere. These polymers separated out of the environmental medium as microdroplets —prebiological systems—very early in chemical evolution. Through abrupt but small qualitative changes, these precellular structures became more and more complex both chemically and morphologically. During this period of separate existence, these structures followed a different chemical evolutionary course than the chemistry of the medium, leading to biochemicals, biochemical pathways, and eventually to cells.

DID LIFE START AS A GENE?

A different approach to the origin of life is given by the gene concept. This theory was proposed by Muller in 1926 in an address before the International Congress of Plant Sciences, but was first published in 1929.[7] He has restated it on many occasions, the latest in 1966.[8] The essence of the theory is that life originated as a gene by the accidental combination of its constituent atoms in the proper order and that the gene is the basis of all life past and present. This theory has its origin in the "living molecule" or "moleculobiont" theory of the origin of life proposed by Troland[9] in 1914.

Troland wrote: "Let us suppose that at a certain moment in earth-history, when the ocean waters are yet warm, there suddenly appears at a definite point within the oceanic body a small amount of a certain catalyzer or enzyme." And further, "The original enzyme was the outcome of a chemical reaction, that is to say, it must have depended upon the collision and combination of separate atoms or molecules, and it is a fact well known among physicists and chemists that the occurrence and specific nature of such collisions can be predicted only by use of the so-called *laws of chance*." ... "Consequently we are forced to say that the production of the original life enzyme was a chance event." And again, "The striking fact that the enzymic theory of life's origin, as we have outlined it, necessitates the spontaneous production of only a single molecule of the original catalyst, renders the objection of improbability almost absurd ... and when one of these enzymes first appeared, bare of all body, in the aboriginal seas it followed as a consequence of its characteristic regulative nature that the phenomenon of life came too."

This was a remarkable paper for its time, the more so since Troland, a physicist, launched a critical reproach against contemporary biologists who had taken a strong vitalistic stand on the subject of life. In Troland's words, "The last years of the nineteenth and first of the twentieth century, which have constituted a period of tremendous progress in physical science, have unfortunately witnessed a recrudescence of that 'cult of incompetence' in biology, *vitalism*. Neo-vitalism under the leadership of Driesch in Germany and of Bergson in France, asserts that phenomena of life are not determined by law-abiding forces, but by a form of activity the effects of which are unpredictable, and which consequently, must be regarded from a formal point of view as chaotic and beyond the range of science."

"It is the purpose of the present paper to combat the thesis of the new vitalism by showing how a single physico-chemical conception may be employed in the rational explanation of the very life-phenomena which the neo-vitalists regard as inexplicable on any but mystical grounds." Troland's ideas are the basis of the "naked gene" theory of the origin of life.

In 1929 Alexander and Bridges,[10] greatly influenced by Troland, further elaborated Muller's gene theory of the origin of life and Alexander again presented the case in 1942 and 1948.[11] Horowitz[12] has been a staunch supporter of the gene theory of the origin of life. More recently Wooldridge[13] integrated the gene theory and the coacervate theory in a mechanistic explanation of life and its origin.

The gene theory is based on remote accidental occurrences and is therefore not susceptible to experimental proof. It has had to depend on discoveries stimulated by other theories. For example, at first Troland thought that the first "life-enzyme" was the accidental coming together of the elements in the right way to form the first moleculobiont. He later modified the theory (1916, 1917) to bring it in line with developments in the then young science of genetics; the "life-enzyme" became the gene—the chemical nature of the gene later being proposed as nucleic acid rather than protein. Further modifications were actually minor until Oparin's theory was put to a test. When the ensuing experiments showed the possibility of the abiotic formation of nucleotides among a host of other organic chemicals, the origin of the gene then was proposed as an accidental coming together of the proper nucleotides in the proper sequence to produce the first coded molecule of deoxyribonucleic acid.

On the surface, the moleculobiont or the gene theory would appear to be the ultimate in mechanistic explanations of life and its origin. Actually, the living molecule or the gene has been made the repository of all the mystical powers of the "élan vital" of the vitalists. It alone is *the* living substance of living things. All else is but frill, designed by the gene for its own protection and survival, a temporary house to be discarded when its purpose has been served. In modern dress, this has been termed the primacy of the gene. Its collective activities are claimed to hold the explanation of all activities from hydrolysis to mental activity.

We have made a mystical thing of the concept of life. It is still a widespread notion that the step from inanimate matter to the first living thing was a more profound and a more improbable transition than all the subsequent changes into all the subsequent forms of life. This view was especially prevalent when it was believed that there were no organic compounds before there were living things and that only living things could make organic compounds. Since life without organic compounds is inconceivable, the problem of the origin of the first living thing was dismissed as being imponderable. Therefore, the fact that life obviously *did* originate was considered to be a more remarkable phenomenon than the coming to pass of the vast morphological, biochemical, and functional changes which were needed to establish the present order of living things from the very beginning.

In this there is the implication that life is a special something which, when pervading matter, endows it with distinctive properties. In the present era many abiotic, organic chemical events, preliminary to the appearance of living things, have already been elucidated. Still, life is often looked upon as something more than the chemical systems that manifest the properties characterized by that term. This is the result of our holding tenaciously to old ways of thinking through which we continue to interpret new findings. These findings confirm earlier inklings that matter has self-organizing properties,[14]* and that interactions of matter and

*See also quotation from Bastian, p. 11 this book.

energy can bring about more and more complex organizations of matter (Oparin, 1938). In 1957 Bernal[15] put this latter point as follows: "In general, the pattern I propose is one of stages of increasing inner complexity, following one another in order of time, each including in itself structures and processes evolved at the lower levels. The division into stages is not in my opinion an arbitrary one." Further: "One of our major problems is to establish the correct steps inferred from existing metabolism as well as the postulating and checking of other steps which have been subsequently effaced by the success of more efficient biochemical mechanisms."

The thing to bear in mind most urgently is that each level of organization has its own properties by which alone it can best be recognized. Also, each higher level, although incorporating "structures and processes evolved at the lower levels," has new properties not predictable from the properties of the lower level. This is true of the whole progression from fundamental particles, atoms, and molecules to man. Each stage in that progression incorporates structures and properties of the lower level but emerges as a new stage with new properties *and the propensity of arriving at a higher level of organization*. Where does life fit in this progression? Nowhere. It makes little sense to attempt to squeeze anywhere into this gradual sequence of stages of matter a nebulous undefinable something called "life," which presumably breaks this gradual sequence abruptly into two groups— inanimate and living.[16] That would be the essence of vitalism clothed in mechanistic terms.

A MATERIALISTIC OUTLOOK

We recognize a vast variety of forms of life at various levels of structural complexity reflecting a corresponding functional and biochemical complexity. Yet we strive paradoxically to find a single meaningful scientific definition of *all* life. If matter, driven by energy, does go inexorably to higher and higher levels of organization in an unbroken chain, it would be impossible to draw a line so that those systems on one side are all "inanimate" and those on the other side "living." Any serious attempt to do so will drive the line more on the "inanimate" side. One could even reach a point where K. M. Madison's concept of "living" would hold: "things as simple as two inorganic reactions meet the definition."

The terms life and living were at first lay terms and in that context had the vaguest of boundaries. For centuries science has been attempting to sharpen the boundaries; to this day attempts continue unsuccessfully. This marked lack of success is a measure of proof that matter goes through a continuous hierarchy of increasingly complex stages, and that there is indeed one evolution, *the evolution of matter*, even to the level of reasoning power. Some time ago Wald[17] expressed this eloquently in the following words:

"We living things are a late outgrowth of the metabolism of our galaxy. The carbon that enters so importantly into our composition was cooked in the remote past in a dying star. From it at lower temperatures nitrogen and oxygen were formed. These, our indispensable elements, were spewed out into space in the exhalations of red giants and such stellar catastrophes as supernovae, there to be mixed with hydrogen to form eventually the substance of the sun and planets, and ourselves . . . ."

"Judging from our experience upon this planet, such a history, that begins with elementary particles leads, perhaps inevitably, toward a strange and moving end: a creature that knows, a science-making animal, that turns back upon the process that generated him and attempts to understand it. Without his like, the universe could be, but not be known, and that is a poor thing."

"Surely this is a great part of our dignity as men, that we can know, and that through us matter can know itself; that beginning with protons and electrons, out of the womb of time and the vastnesses of space, we can begin to understand; that organized as in us, the hydrogen, the carbon, the nitrogen, the oxygen, those 16 to 21 elements, the water, the sunlight—all, having become us, can begin to understand what they are, and how they came to be."

References

1. S. W. Fox and K. Harada, *J. Amer. Chem. Soc.* **82,** 3745 (1960).
2. K. Harada and S. W. Fox, in "The Origins of Prebiological Systems and of their Molecular Matrices," S. W. Fox (ed.), Academic Press, New York, 1965, p. 187.
3. _____, *Nature* **201,** 335 (1964).
4. K. A. Grossenbacher and C. A. Knight, in "The Origins of Prebiological Systems," S. W. Fox (ed.), Academic Press, New York, 1965, p. 173.
5. S. W. Fox, K. Harada, K. R. Woods, and C. R. Windsor, *Arch. Biochem. Biophys.* **102,** 493 (1963).
6. G. Steinman, *Arch. Biochem. Biophys.* **119,** 96 (1967).
7. H. J. Muller, *Proc. Intern. Cong. Plant Physiol.* **1,** 897 (1929).
8. _____, *The Amer. Naturalist* **100,** 493 (1966).
9. L. T. Troland, *The Monist* **24,** 92 (1914).
10. J. Alexander and C. B. Bridges, *Science* **70,** 508 (1929).
11. J. Alexander, "Life, its Nature and Origin" Reinhold Publishing Corporation, New York, 1948.
12. N. H. Horowitz, *I. U. B. Symp. Series, Vol. 1,* Academic Press, New York, 1959, pp. 106–107.
13. D. E. Wooldridge, "The Machinery of Life," McGraw-Hill Book Company, New York, 1966.
14. G. Wald, *Sci. Am.,* Aug. 1954, p. 44.
15. J. D. Bernal, *I. U. B. Symp. Series, Vol. 1,* Academic Press, New York, 1959, p. 38.
16. E. Kahane, "La Vie N'existe Pas!" Éditions Rationalistes, Paris, 1962.
17. G. Wald, *Proc. Natl. Acad. Sciences* **52,** 595 (1964).

chapter nine

Some Other Problems and Speculations

ASYMMETRIC SYNTHESIS

If a carbon atom has a different substituent at each of its four bonds, it is said to form an asymmetric center in the molecule and the compound in which it is located can exist in either of two mirror-image forms (enantiomorphic states). For example, the amino acid alanine can exist in the forms

L-Alanine   D-Alanine

in which the middle carbon atom is the asymmetric center and the —NH$_2$ and —H are in mirror-image position to each other. As previously mentioned, one finds almost exclusively L- but not D-amino acids and D- but not L-sugars in living things. This is due to the fact that the enzymes mediating in these syntheses are correspondingly asymmetric. In laboratory synthesis (and also in nature), when no asymmetric forces are involved, the configuration around an asymmetric center is at random, and racemic mixtures (equal amounts of each enantiomorph) result. Therefore, the question is: How did the chemical asymmetry in living things come about in the first place? Several explanations have been offered.

Natural Asymmetric Forces

One line of explanation involves the search for some asymmetric force in nature under which the synthesis of one enantiomorph would be favored. It has been suggested that circularly polarized light, as that reflected from the moon, or plane polarized light, as that reflected from the sea, are such forces. But the excess in the direction of polarization in either case is very small. Circularly and plane polarized light and other natural "forces," such as left- or right-oriented crystal surfaces, asymmetric catalysts, etc., have been considered and discarded by Wald.[1] Oparin, however, puts much emphasis on the few cases of asymmetric synthesis by polarized light and asymmetric catalysts.[2] In Bernal's hypothesis of organic chemosynthesis on clays, the possible presence of asymmetric catalysts or mineral surfaces in the clays could play a role in asymmetric synthesis. Gabriel[3] calls attention to inclusion compounds, which are formed by some substances when they crystallize in such fashion as to enclose an internal space or cage with specific dimensions. "Guest" molecules of complementary configuration can become enclosed therein. The configuration of the cage of a host inclusion compound may accomodate one member of a pair of enantiomorphic substances but not the other. In this way physical resolution of a racemic mixture may take place. Chemical resolution of racemic mixtures has also been demonstrated.[4]

Stereospecific Synthesis

Natta[5] obtained stereospecific polymerization with synthetic organometallic catalysts that exist in enantiomorphic pairs. This differs from the usual abiotic synthesis, in which both isomers result in equal numbers from the same catalyst, making it impossible to separate such a process into different stereoisomeric syntheses. In Natta's method this separation is conceivable and, as he pointed out, isolation of the asymmetric active centers corresponding to only one of the two isomers "could solve the problem of asymmetric organic synthesis in the field of macromolecules."[6]

Harada[7] reported the nonenzymic synthesis of L-alanine, $[\alpha]_D^{27} = +13.99°$ (95 percent optically active). The method was essentially a Strecker synthesis which is considered to be a possible method of abiogenic amino acid formation on the primitive earth. More recently he has pursued this and similar lines of the synthesis of optically active alpha-amino acids.[8-11] His references cite earlier and contemporary works.

Resolution by Competition Among Organisms

Another line of explanation is the assumption that the optical isomers now found in living things were included by chance by the first living organism and have since been handed down from generation to generation. Life arose not as a single case but probably repetitively at the time of its origin. Chance incorporation of optical isomers would establish some forms with L-amino acid and D-sugar composition and others with D-amino acids and L-sugars. However, there is a distinct advantage in having one type of food chain for all organisms. This advantage would be realized if one type of organism developed a favorable mutation (not necessarily associated with optical activity), for such an advantage would endow this type with a higher survival rate. The favored type, with all of its characteristics, including optical activity, would eventually replace the other. This is the way Wald proposes that the present situation came about; in essence, it was "natural selection on the molecular level."[1]

THE METEORITE QUESTION

Did the parent body of meteorites harbor life? Evidence for "biogenic activity" in carbonaceous chondrites has been presented (see pp. 22–24). This evidence has met with determined resistance from some quarters. One might wonder why—especially since many respected workers and thinkers in this problem are convinced, without any tangible evidence, that life is universal, that it is an inevitable outcome of the operation of natural laws.

Objections are raised mainly on the grounds of validity— Are the findings real and significant? If so: Are explanations other than "biogenic activity" possible? The discovery of extraterrestrial life would have enormous scientific, philosophical, and religious implications. It is not to be wondered then, that hard-headed scientists approach the claims with skepticism. Yet the claimants themselves are highly responsible scientists who have answered the criticisms with experiments designed to overcome the stated objections. The implications do demand that the evidence be unequivocal.

OUTLINE OF THE METEORITE CONTROVERSY

The present controversy started with an article by Nagy, Meinschein, and Hennessy in 1961.[12] These authors analyzed the organic material in the Orgueil meteorite and cautiously concluded: "Based on these preliminary studies, the composition of the hydrocarbons in the Orgueil meteorite provide evidence for biogenic activity." The organic compounds found earlier in the Murray carbonaceous chondrite[13] were interpreted by the authors (Calvin and Vaughn, 1960) as being the result of abiotic synthesis prior to the origin of life. The points in controversy are the resemblance of meteoritic hydrocarbons to hydrocarbons of undisputed biological origin, the detection of optical activity in the organic compounds of meteorites, and the presence of microscopic "organized elements" which might be interpreted as fossils of one-time living microorganisms.

The first question raised is that of contamination. Carbonaceous chondrites are porous. The samples examined have rested in museum cases for many decades. In addition to possible contamination on contact first with the atmosphere and then with the surface of the earth, further contamination would occur each time the atmospheric pressure changed, causing air to enter and leave the porous meteorite. This passive "breathing" would subject the meteorite to constant contamination by various kinds of earthly gases and dust.[14] Nagy and his co-workers modified their techniques and applied even more accurate analytical methods to the problem to meet this and other objections. We now have a fair amount of assurance that at least some of the reported organic compounds are indigenous to the meteorites. But the interpretation that these were synthesized on the parent body of the carbonaceous chondrites has recently been challenged by the claim that fairly complex organic compounds probably were, and are being synthesized in space.[15,16] (Fig. 9-1, Table 9-1). Organic compounds may have formed a part of the material which condensed to form any celestial body—including the earth. This hypothesis precipitated an exchange of views[17] in a highly critical vein between the authors and their disputants.

Even greater controversy has arisen over the question of detectable levo-rotation in the organic fraction of meteorites. Optical activity is generally taken as an evidence of biological activity. The report by Nagy, et al.[18] of the presence of optical activity in the organic matter of the Orgueil meteorite was discounted by others on various grounds. Hayatsu[19] was not able to confirm the claim and attributed the slight levo-rotation, reported by Nagy, to the presence of colloidal sulfur and the limitations of the instrument. Both of these sources of error have been pointed out by others.[20-23] The role of contamination in determinations of optical activity was also suggested.[24] In a recent paper, Nagy[25] re-examined

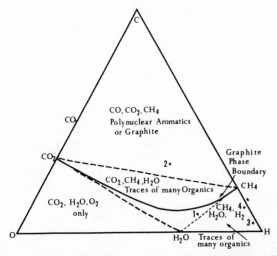

Fig. 9-1. Thermodynamic Equilibria in Atmospheres of Varying Elemental Proportions. The solid curve indicates the phase boundary along which graphite becomes stable at atm. and 500°K. Above the line CH_4—CO_2, equilibrium favors the formation of large proportions of polycyclic aromatic compounds. The numbered asterisks indicate the compositions of the equilibrium distributions shown in Table 9-1. After R. V. Eck, et al., Science **153**, *628 (1966).*

the organic matter of the Orgueil meteorite, avoiding most of the indicated sources of error, and insists that his findings are real "... but the origin of this effect can not yet be satisfactorily explained. It is possible that the optical activity of meteorite lipids are the result of terrestrial contaminations and/or that they are extraterrestrial and indigenous." This important question must also be considered still open to an impartial evaluation.

There is, finally, the interesting question of the presence of "organized elements" which can be construed as fossils of one-time living microorganisms (Fig. 9-2). The original claim by Claus and Nagy[26] and Nagy, et al.[27] was refuted by Fitch and Anders[28-29] in 1963, after the latter authors made

TABLE 9-1. Mole Fraction Compositions of Compounds in Equilibrium. The Relative Abundances of C, H, and O for the Four Points are shown in Fig. 9-1. N is as Abundant as C. Cl and S are 0.0001 Per Cent as Abundant as C. Temperatures of 1000°K and Pressures of 1 Atm or 10^{-6} Atm are Considered. The Four Composition Points Have the Following C:H:O Ratios: Point 1, 10:70:20; Point 2, 30:50:20; Point 3, 4:94:2; Point 4, 12:86:2.

Elemental composition point	1 Atm				10^{-6} Atm			
	1	2	3	4	1	2	3	4
H_2	0.54	0.11	0.86	0.55	0.55	0.37	0.91	0.81
O_2	$.59 \times 10^{-21}$	$.57 \times 10^{-26}$	$.15 \times 10^{-23}$	$.37 \times 10^{-25}$	$.52 \times 10^{-18}$	$.99 \times 10^{-35}$	$.25 \times 10^{-66}$	$.21 \times 10^{-36}$
H_2O	.15	$.92 \times 10^{-4}$	$.12 \times 10^{-1}$	$.12 \times 10^{-2}$	.15	$.14 \times 10^{-10}$	$.53 \times 10^{-11}$	$.43 \times 10^{-11}$
CO_2	$.55 \times 10^{-1}$	$.48 \times 10^{-3}$	$.56 \times 10^{-3}$	$.15 \times 10^{-3}$	$.53 \times 10^{-1}$	$.17 \times 10^{-10}$	$.32 \times 10^{-12}$	$.30 \times 10^{-12}$
CO	.14	.40	$.28 \times 10^{-1}$	$.48 \times 10^{-1}$	.15	.34	$.39 \times 10^{-1}$	$.41 \times 10^{-1}$
CH_4	$.55 \times 10^{-2}$	.19	$.55 \times 10^{-1}$	.25	$.63 \times 10^{-14}$	$.49 \times 10^{-4}$	$.21 \times 10^{-8}$	$.19 \times 10^{-3}$
C_2H_6	$.11 \times 10^{-7}$	$.68 \times 10^{-4}$	$.70 \times 10^{-6}$	$.22 \times 10^{-4}$	$.14 \times 10^{-31}$	$.13 \times 10^{-11}$	$.96 \times 10^{-11}$	$.89 \times 10^{-11}$
N_2	.10	.30	$.42 \times 10^{-1}$	.15	.10	.25	$.37 \times 10^{-1}$	.12
NH_2	$.69 \times 10^{-4}$	$.10 \times 10^{-4}$	$.89 \times 10^{-4}$	$.86 \times 10^{-4}$	$.70 \times 10^{-10}$	$.62 \times 10^{-10}$	$.91 \times 10^{-10}$	$.14 \times 10^{-9}$
HCN	$.41 \times 10^{-6}$	$.28 \times 10^{-3}$	$.13 \times 10^{-5}$	$.21 \times 10^{-4}$	$.45 \times 10^{-12}$	$.10 \times 10^{-1}$	$.43 \times 10^{-2}$	$.82 \times 10^{-2}$
Benzene	$.20 \times 10^{-18}$	$.76 \times 10^{-3}$	$.29 \times 10^{-14}$	$.12 \times 10^{-8}$	$< 10^{-36}$	$.28 \times 10^{-5}$	$.53 \times 10^{-5}$	$.84 \times 10^{-5}$
Naphthalene	$.88 \times 10^{-30}$	$.41 \times 10^{-3}$	$.48 \times 10^{-23}$	$.18 \times 10^{-13}$	$< 10^{-38}$	$.11 \times 10^{-5}$	$.13 \times 10^{-5}$	$.31 \times 10^{-5}$
"Asphalt"	$< 10^{-38}$	$.33 \times 10^{-4}$	$< 10^{-38}$	$.46 \times 10^{-29}$	$< 10^{-38}$	$.68 \times 10^{-2}$	$.86 \times 10^{-2}$	$.80 \times 10^{-2}$
Formic acid	$.15 \times 10^{-7}$	$.26 \times 10^{-10}$	$.25 \times 10^{-9}$	$.42 \times 10^{-10}$	$.15 \times 10^{-13}$	$.33 \times 10^{-23}$	$.15 \times 10^{-24}$	$.13 \times 10^{-24}$
Acetic acid	$.24 \times 10^{-10}$	$.70 \times 10^{-11}$	$.24 \times 10^{-11}$	$.28 \times 10^{-11}$	$.26 \times 10^{-28}$	$.66 \times 10^{-28}$	$.52 \times 10^{-29}$	$.44 \times 10^{-29}$
Formaldehyde	$.10 \times 10^{-6}$	$.54 \times 10^{-6}$	$.32 \times 10^{-7}$	$.34 \times 10^{-7}$	$.10 \times 10^{-12}$	$.17 \times 10^{-12}$	$.47 \times 10^{-13}$	$.43 \times 10^{-13}$
Methanol	$.24 \times 10^{-8}$	$.25 \times 10^{-9}$	$.12 \times 10^{-8}$	$.85 \times 10^{-9}$	$.26 \times 10^{-20}$	$.28 \times 10^{-20}$	$.19 \times 10^{-20}$	$.16 \times 10^{-20}$
Ethanol	$.34 \times 10^{-13}$	$.63 \times 10^{-12}$	$.11 \times 10^{-12}$	$.52 \times 10^{-13}$	$.41 \times 10^{-37}$	$.50 \times 10^{-27}$	$.60 \times 10^{-27}$	$.50 \times 10^{-27}$
Ethylene	$.72 \times 10^{-8}$	$.22 \times 10^{-3}$	$.28 \times 10^{-6}$	$.14 \times 10^{-4}$	$.90 \times 10^{-26}$	$.12 \times 10^{-5}$	$.36 \times 10^{-5}$	$.38 \times 10^{-5}$

Acetylene	$.27 \times 10^{-10}$	$.42 \times 10^{-5}$	$.65 \times 10^{-9}$	$.49 \times 10^{-7}$	$.33 \times 10^{-22}$	$.64 \times 10^{-2}$	$.80 \times 10^{-2}$	$.93 \times 10^{-2}$
Xylene	$.16 \times 10^{-27}$	$.19 \times 10^{-7}$	$.88 \times 10^{-22}$	$.18 \times 10^{-14}$	$< 10^{-38}$	$.37 \times 10^{-18}$	$.21 \times 10^{-17}$	$.35 \times 10^{-17}$
Acetone	$.97 \times 10^{-15}$	$.16 \times 10^{-10}$	$.12 \times 10^{-13}$	$.63 \times 10^{-12}$	$< 10^{-38}$	$.27 \times 10^{-24}$	$.23 \times 10^{-24}$	$.22 \times 10^{-24}$
Dimethyl ether	$.81 \times 10^{-12}$	$.15 \times 10^{-11}$	$.26 \times 10^{-12}$	$.12 \times 10^{-11}$	$.97 \times 10^{-37}$	$.12 \times 10^{-28}$	$.14 \times 10^{-26}$	$.12 \times 10^{-26}$
Methylamine	$.23 \times 10^{-11}$	$.58 \times 10^{-10}$	$.18 \times 10^{-10}$	$.12 \times 10^{-9}$	$.26 \times 10^{-29}$	$.26 \times 10^{-19}$	$.67 \times 10^{-19}$	$.10 \times 10^{-18}$
Glycine	$.88 \times 10^{-20}$	$.20 \times 10^{-20}$	$.73 \times 10^{-21}$	$.13 \times 10^{-20}$	$< 10^{-38}$	$< 10^{-38}$	$< 10^{-38}$	$< 10^{-38}$
Pyridine	$.81 \times 10^{-22}$	$.14 \times 10^{-8}$	$.15 \times 10^{-18}$	$.14 \times 10^{-13}$	$< 10^{-38}$	$.12 \times 10^{-12}$	$.77 \times 10^{-13}$	$.20 \times 10^{-12}$
S_2	$.74 \times 10^{-9}$	$.12 \times 10^{-6}$	$.50 \times 10^{-10}$	$.15 \times 10^{-8}$	$.32 \times 10^{-3}$	$.88 \times 10^{-7}$	$.18 \times 10^{-7}$	$.51 \times 10^{-7}$
CS_2	$.12 \times 10^{-8}$	$.17 \times 10^{-3}$	$.31 \times 10^{-9}$	$.98 \times 10^{-7}$	$.55 \times 10^{-9}$	$.26 \times 10^{-2}$	$.39 \times 10^{-3}$	$.12 \times 10^{-3}$
H_2S	$.20 \times 10^{-2}$	$.50 \times 10^{-2}$	$.84 \times 10^{-3}$	$.29 \times 10^{-2}$	$.14 \times 10^{-2}$	$.15 \times 10^{-4}$	$.17 \times 10^{-4}$	$.25 \times 10^{-4}$
SO_2	$.20 \times 10^{-10}$	$.25 \times 10^{-14}$	$.14 \times 10^{-13}$	$.18 \times 10^{-14}$	$.12 \times 10^{-4}$	$.37 \times 10^{-26}$	$.44 \times 10^{-28}$	$.59 \times 10^{-28}$
COS	$.17 \times 10^{-4}$	$.59 \times 10^{-8}$	$.87 \times 10^{-6}$	$.80 \times 10^{-5}$	$.11 \times 10^{-4}$	$.44 \times 10^{-6}$	$.23 \times 10^{-7}$	$.40 \times 10^{-7}$
Methanethiol	$.20 \times 10^{-8}$	$.86 \times 10^{-8}$	$.51 \times 10^{-8}$	$.13 \times 10^{-6}$	$.15 \times 10^{-20}$	$.19 \times 10^{-12}$	$.38 \times 10^{-12}$	$.57 \times 10^{-12}$
Benzenethiol	$.12 \times 10^{-22}$	$.56 \times 10^{-7}$	$.45 \times 10^{-20}$	$.10 \times 10^{-13}$	$< 10^{-38}$	$.18 \times 10^{-12}$	$.16 \times 10^{-12}$	$.41 \times 10^{-12}$
Thiophene	$.20 \times 10^{-17}$	$.63 \times 10^{-6}$	$.32 \times 10^{-15}$	$.98 \times 10^{-11}$	$< 10^{-38}$	$.13 \times 10^{-8}$	$.92 \times 10^{-9}$	$.21 \times 10^{-8}$
Cl_2	$.24 \times 10^{-18}$	$.11 \times 10^{-12}$	$.26 \times 10^{-16}$	$.50 \times 10^{-15}$	$.23 \times 10^{-15}$	$.23 \times 10^{-14}$	$.22 \times 10^{-16}$	$.24 \times 10^{-15}$
HCl	$.20 \times 10^{-2}$	$.59 \times 10^{-2}$	$.84 \times 10^{-3}$	$.29 \times 10^{-2}$	$.20 \times 10^{-2}$	$.51 \times 10^{-2}$	$.77 \times 10^{-3}$	$.24 \times 10^{-2}$
CH_3Cl	$.69 \times 10^{-9}$	$.36 \times 10^{-6}$	$.18 \times 10^{-8}$	$.44 \times 10^{-7}$	$.77 \times 10^{-21}$	$.23 \times 10^{-10}$	$.61 \times 10^{-11}$	$.19 \times 10^{-40}$
CCl_4	$.35 \times 10^{-33}$	$.62 \times 10^{-27}$	$.16 \times 10^{-24}$	$.63 \times 10^{-31}$	$< 10^{-38}$	$.58 \times 10^{-33}$	$.38 \times 10^{-37}$	$.51 \times 10^{-35}$

From R. V. Eck, et al., *Science* **153**, 628 (1966).

careful biological and chemical examinations of a large number of "organized elements" in samples of the Orgueil and Ivuna meteorites. They found that the most interesting "organized elements"—those showing an internal organization of particles—could be written off as pollen and as mold spore contaminants, acquired in the course of processing. Other organized elements were structureless and, although indigenous to the meteorites, they could possibly be of inorganic origin according to these authors. Further studies by Nagy et al.[30] tend to validate the claim that many of the organized elements are indigenous to the meteorite and are not the result of contamination at any time. Tasch[31] in 1964, after a careful morphological study with suitable controls, concluded that some 12 types of structured "organized elements" were native to the meteorite samples and were not introduced from the air *during* the course of the experiments. However, no conclusion could be reached as to whether or not these were terrestrial contaminants which entered the meteorite during the decades *prior* to the present investigations.

Urey[32] in a recent review pointed out that the parent body of the meteorites could not have had sufficient water for the chemical evolution that has to precede the origin of life, and for life itself after its origination. Therefore, if organized elements do represent fossil microorganisms (which he does not discount), they could not have arisen on the parent body. He suggests "that life evolved on one planetary object and that it was transferred to another planetary object of primitive composition." In this regard he proposes specifically the earth-moon relationship, and suggests that the source of meteorites would be the moon "which may have a composition consistent with the carbonaceous chondrites for all we know. It is an old suggestion that meteorites have been coming from the moon, but the recent evidence, though not conclusive, is suggestive at least." He also cautioned that skepticism does not warrant summary rejection. "It seems

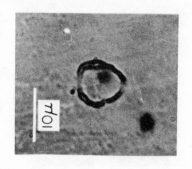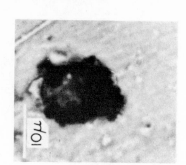

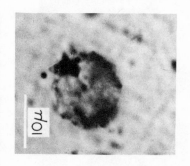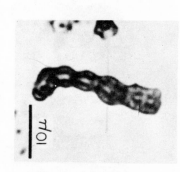

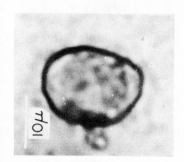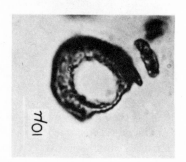

Fig. 9-2. Photomicrographs of various types of organized elements from the Orgueil Meteorite. Courtesy B. Nagy.

101

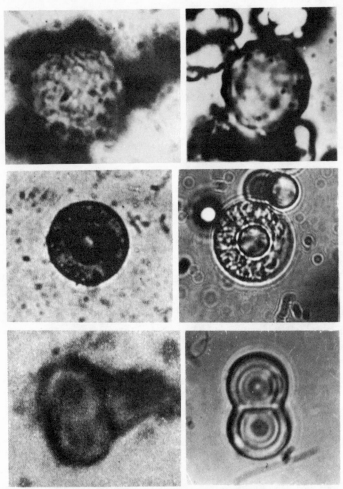

Fig. 9-3. Formed Elements from carbonaceous chondrite (left) and comparable microspheres (right). From S. W. Fox, BioScience **14**, 16 (1964).

that we should be willing to consider the evidence for a residue of life in meteorites objectively, and that we should not draw final negative conclusions before all the evidence has been secured." Later he added "However if the residue of indigenous biological activity in meteorites is indeed real, and if meteorites do not come from the moon, other more complicated and perhaps more interesting histories for these objects must be devised." And "... people who obviously hope that life has existed in these objects should be encouraged to secure definite, positive evidence if they are able to do so." Nagy[33] recently prepared a survey of the various investigations of the Orgueil meteorite.

Fox[34] has called attention to the fact that in size and appearance many types of "organized elements" resemble his own proteinoid microspheres. The selected examples (Fig. 9-3) do indeed show a remarkable resemblance. This could be interpreted in the following way. The primitive parent body of the carbonaceous chondrites had a chemical history similar to that of the primitive earth; namely, proteinoids were synthesized early in chemical evolution, and these gave rise to microspheres of all kinds. In this interpretation the "organized elements" of meteorites represent fossilized precellular structures and not microorganisms. This explanation of the presence of "organized elements" may mean that chemical evolution on the parent body did not quite reach the stage of life's origin.

NEOBIOGENESIS

The first origin of life anywhere requires a preliminary chemical history during which organic compounds form abiotically. Life is then fashioned from the organic medium under proper environmental conditions. But once the appropriate medium and conditions are established the eventual formation of self-replicating chemical systems (primitive living things) therefrom becomes an event of high probability. Reflecting this concept, many authors prefer the plural "*origins* of life" to designate this process, implying that not one, but a variety of conditions can engender life; that those conditions can bring about not just a solitary example but multitudes of first primitive living things.

All manner of chemical and physical conditions have existed since the first origin of life, making its reorigin (neobiogenesis) a continuing possibility. The arguments against neobiogenesis reflect many misunderstandings. Neobiogenesis is erroneously equated with spontaneous generation. Gratuitous assumptions are made that the first living thing was a unique physico-chemical system that required unique conditions which can exist for only a fleeting era in the history of a planet. The apparent unity of biochemistry among all living things is taken as evidence for a single line of descent from a first living thing. These and other arguments do not appear to be valid[35-37] in the light of the newer information on the chemical origin of life.

The immediate prerequisites for the origin of living things according to either the gene theory or the prebiological systems theory have existed ever since the first appearance of living things. In the gene theory, the prerequisites are supplies of various deoxynucleotides. But with the origin of the first "coded" nucleic acid, the possibility arose that fragments of DNA might become established as separate living things distinct from the original. In the prebiological systems theory, the prerequisites are microscopic structures embodying complex coordinated reactions and pathways. The mechanical disruption of cells which occurs endlessly in nature affords a never-ending supply of the simplest to the most complex systems of this kind. The only question that remains is whether such fragments (pieces of genetic code or cytoplasmic fragments embodying coordinated chemical reactions of various kinds) are the proper material to serve as the starting point for experiments on the origin of life by nature or in the laboratory.

SUMMARY
Much of the research on the problem of the origin of life is

still directed toward the synthesis of biochemical compounds under simulated primitive earth conditions. The formation of amino acids, polypeptides, adenine, guanine, nucleosides, nucleotides, nucleic acids, sugars, aldehydes, and organic acids has been well documented. Uracil, porphyrins, urea, and a number of non-biological organic compounds have also been reported. Frequently, one or more polymeric substances are mentioned.

This interest in abiotically synthesized biochemicals parallels the prevalent belief that life was established after the appearance of a large variety of biochemicals which were then assembled into the structure of the first primitive living thing. In this theory the formation of microscopic droplets — precellular systems — is an intermediate step between chemicals and cells.

A great deal of interest is beginning to center on reaction mechanisms. An understanding of the manner of formation of the various organic compounds from primitive gases could shed light on the origin of biochemical pathways. It is too early to make definitive statements in this regard. Amino acids apparently form readily from methane (or carbon monoxide), ammonia and water. A Strecker-type synthesis, in which various nitriles are formed which on hydrolysis yield the corresponding amino acids is likely. More attention is being focused on the role of hydrogen cyanide in the formation of biochemicals. This compound forms an active biradical which can polymerize into purines, sugars, and also into protein backbones.

A knotty problem has been the mechanism of protein formation through the polymerization of amino acids in an aqueous medium where hydrolysis, not polymerization, is favored. Calvin and his co-workers have shown that dicyandiamide, derived from hydrogen cyanide and ammonia, favors polymerization of amino acids in an aqueous medium. On the other hand, Fox has always been a staunch proponent of the thermal polymerization of amino acids under anhydrous conditions, thus avoiding the thermodynamic barrier presented by water.

The meteorite question, which arose in 1961 and 1962, has entered an interesting phase. Considerable evidence has been adduced for the presence of a variety of organic compounds as indigenous components of carbonaceous chondrites. Microscopic structures, termed "organized elements," which might be fossil microorganisms, have also been described in these meteorites. The suggestions that both the organic compounds and the "organized elements" are evidences of "biogenic activity" in the meteorites are under sharp criticism. A number of other controversies are examined: the nature of the primitive atmosphere, energy forms, the gene as the basis and origin of life, asymmetric synthesis, and neobiogenesis. A suggestion is also forwarded that biochemistry evolved primarily in prebiological systems concomitantly with the morphological developments that carried these systems to the level of cells.

References

1. G. Wald, *Ann. N.Y. Acad. Sci.* **69**, 352 (1957).
2. A. I. Oparin, "Origin of Life," Academic Press, New York, 1957, pp. 189–196.
3. M. Gabriel, *Am. Naturalist* **94**, 257 (1960).
4. S. Winstein and H. J. Lucas, *J. Am. Chem. Soc.* **61**, 1576 (1939).
5. G. Natta, P. Pino, G. Mazzanti, and P. Longi, *Gazz. chim. ital.* **88**, 219 (1958).
6. G. Natta, *J. Inorg. & Nuclear Chem.* **8**, 589 (1958).
7. K. Harada, *Nature* **200**, 1201 (1963).
8. _____, *Nature* **212**, 1571 (1966).
9. _____, *J. Org. Chem.* (March 1967).
10. _____, ibidem (May 1967).
11. _____, ibid in press (July 1967).
12. B. Nagy, W. G. Meinschein, and D. J. Hennessy, *Ann. N.Y. Acad. Sci.* **93**, 25 (1961).

13. M. Calvin and S. K. Vaugh, in *Proc. First Internatl. Space Science Symp.*, H. Kallmann, (ed.), North Holland Publishing Company, Amsterdam, 1960, pp. 1171–1191.

14. E. Anders, *Ann. N.Y. Acad. Sci.* **93**, 651 (1962).

15. R. V. Eck, E. R. Lippincott, M. O. Dayhoff and Y. T. Pratt, *Science* **153**, 628 (1966).

16. M. H. Studier, R. Hayatsu, and E. Anders, *Science* **149**, 1455 (1965).

17. "Organic Matter in Carbonaceous Chondrites," Letters to the Editor, *Science* **152**, 102 (1966).

18. B. Nagy, Sister M. T. J. Murphy, V. E. Modzeleski, G. Rouser, G. Claus, D. J. Hennessy, U. Colombo, and F. Gazzarinni, *Nature* **202**, 228 (1964).

19. R. Hayatsu, *Science* **149**, 443 (1965).

20. A. L. Rouy, B. Carroll, and T. J. Quigley, *Anal. Chem.* **35**, 627 (1963).

21. A. L. Rouy and B. Carroll, *Anal. Chem.* **38**, 1367 (1966).

22. _____, *Nature* **212**, 1458 (1966).

23. R. Hayatsu, *Science* **153**, 859 (1966).

24. W. G. Meinschein, C. Frondel, P. Laur, and K. Kislow, *Science* **154**, 377 (1966).

25. B. Nagy, *Proc. Natl. Acad. Sci.* **56**, 389 (1966).

26. G. Claus and B. Nagy, *Nature* **192**, 594 (1961).

27. B. Nagy, G. Claus, and D. J. Hennessy, *Nature* **193**, 1129 (1962).

28. F. W. Fitch and E. Anders, *Science* **140**, 1097 (1963).

29. _____, *Ann. N.Y. Acad. Sci.* **108**, 495 (1963).

30. B. Nagy, et al., *Nature* **198**, 121 (1963).

31. P. Tasch, *Ann. N.Y. Acad. Sci.* **105**, 927 (1964).

32. H. C. Urey, *Science* **151**, 157 (1966).

33. B. Nagy, *Geol. Fören. I Stockholm Förhand.* **88**, 235 (1966).

34. S. W. Fox, *BioScience* **14**, 13 (1964).

35. J. Keosian, *Science* **131**, 479 (1960).

36. _____, in "An Encyclopedia of the Biological Sciences," P. Gray (ed.), Reinhold Publishing Corporation, New York, 1961.

37. _____, "The Origin of Life," (first ed.) Reinhold Publishing Corporation, New York, 1964, pp. 98–111.

chapter ten

The Extraterrestrial Life Question

If the question about the origin of his own and other forms of life has puzzled man from time immemorial, the question of life in the universe could only be asked after a number of hurdles of psychological, religious, and ultimately, scientific nature had been taken. The psychological barrier has been likened to the "only child syndrome," where man hugged the belief that he, as the center of the universe, was situated upon a central, unmoving earth of immense size. Around him revolved the sun, the moon, and the stars, solely for his comfort and enjoyment; he was not eager to give up this vantage point, or worse yet, to *share* his exalted condition with similar beings from distant worlds. Only isolated dreamers, poets, and thinkers would sometime find solace rather than diminishment in the idea that there could be companions for life's adventure as far away as the stars.

When Copernicus' calculations indicated that a universe with the sun at its center would prove more manageable, religious objections to this change in perspective from the time-hallowed geocentric view made it very unhealthy to agree with the new concept. Thus, Ptolemy's synthesis of the Aristotelian construct, where stars and planets in concentric crystalline spheres circled around the stationary earth, continued to hold sway until the seventeenth century. It took Newton's law of universal gravitation to make the heliocentric universe fully respectable, and it took Darwin's theory of evolution to depose man from his central position on earth.

As time went by, increasingly refined and improved telescopes allowed more and more revealing glimpses into the space around us and ever farther beyond. Recently, the visual information has been rounded out and enhanced by the giant listening ears of radio telescopes, so that by now most of us can take with philosophic equanimity the fact that even our entire solar system amounts to only a small blob swirling near the edge of our Milky Way, which, in turn, is merely one of a multitude of galaxies in a universe of unimaginable vastness.

That certainly pin-points our position. But what of life beyond our planet? And most interesting to us, what are the chances of intelligent life out there somewhere, and contact with it? As we shall see, definite answers to these questions cannot be given as yet. But a confrontation with extraterrestrial intelligent beings, most likely representatives of far-advanced civilizations, is already viewed with misgivings. It is feared that such an experience would precipitate a "cult of despair" at the realization that we are not even nearly as highly evolved as we had imagined in our fond dreams of uniqueness.

To attack the question of life in the universe in a scientific manner it was first necessary to study the conditions under which life could arise, and where in the world it could happen. This led to questions about the origin of galaxies, stars, and planets, and to the most basic problem—how *all of it* started.

Cosmology, the study of the structure and evolution of the universe, is heavily dependent upon astronomy, which obviously has to be based on indirect evidence, obtained, as Shapley says, by using telescopes and brains. Improved instrumentation, orbiting observatories, and the soon-to-be-realized manned landings on the moon and nearer planets promise to narrow the gap between direct and indirect information. But already many educated guesses and fascinating hypotheses are being poured into this gap, concerning the age (eternal?) and the limits (infinite?) of the universe. These questions could be attempted only because of advances in nuclear research which make it possible to measure the relative abundances of elements for age determinations of celestial bodies, and for approximate distance scales. Still, the tremendous difficulty of making observational evaluations of the various hypotheses leaves the choice of the most fitting model of the universe wide open.

In the 1920's Einstein postulated a closed universe of "positive" curvature. Shortly afterwards, Hubble discovered the "red shift" which suggests that the universe is rapidly expanding, and thereby straightening the curvature like a growing soap bubble. Abbé Lemaître inferred from this that the galaxies once were much closer to each other, and that some 12 billion years ago the entire material universe was balled together into a "cosmic egg" of enormous density. At least five billion years ago this "superatom" exploded with a "big bang" and is still flying apart with increasing speed. This evolutionary hypothesis has been avidly taken up and popularized by Gamov.

A more recent hypothesis of an expanding universe, advanced by Oskar Klein and advocated by Hannes Alfvén,[1-2] seems to have stepped right out of the pages of science fiction. Like the "big bang" it starts with an explosion, but this one is caused by the annihilation of colliding particles of matter and anti-matter. The ensuing expansion is driven by radiation pressure. Although the mind reels at the possibility of the existence of "anti-worlds," and thus "anti-life," and many questions remain to be answered, this theory seems to agree well with a number of physical and observational aspects.

The "steady state" universe, suggested by Gold and elaborated by Hoyle, rests on the "perfect cosmological principle" that the universe looks about the same from any point in space or time. This could not hold if the receding galaxies left holes of decreased density; to compensate for such expansionary depletion, the continuous creation of matter at a low rate has been postulated. So far, however, neither infinitely old nor newly created galactic material has been observed. Moreover, recent findings point to the presence of greater amounts of intergalactic dust in the past. Thus, here too, any definite conclusions would be premature.

All the various cosmologies agree, though, that the original matter of the universe was hydrogen, the "mother atom" (Shapley). And, so far, only religion can answer where *that* came from. But some theorists believe that clusters of protogalaxies, galaxies, and stars were separated out from a primordial diffuse hydrogen cloud as it contracted and converted its mounting radiation pressure into kinetic energy. Others prefer to think that far from being a one-time event, new stars are continually arising from interstellar dust.

In recent years it has become possible to document the life history of stars with computerized nuclear measurements. Paralleling the development of galaxies, the stars, too, are thought to begin as opaque cold gas spheres, contracting by gravitational pull, and heating up in the process. The small dark globules observed in gaseous nebulae may be protostars, hot enough for the ionization but not yet for the burning of hydrogen. Radiation, no longer dissipated into space, rapidly accumulates in the protostars until an equilibrium state is reached between radiation pressure and gravitational energy. The contraction holds, and the pent-up forces are converted to heat and light—a star is born!

The hydrogen core is burning now, cooking helium nuclei, and—depending on its initial mass, the star will continue to radiate stably until the hydrogen fuel is used up. Very large and massive stars, like blue giants, will burn up rapidly, in mere millions of years, while stars like our sun may go on for 10–15 billion years. It has been estimated that in about 8 billion years our star will once again start to contract and grow hotter. Only stars of a mass some 10–20 percent greater than ours will run the entire evolutionary course: after hydrogen depletion helium flashes up, producing carbon nuclei. A continuous progression of core contractions accompanied by increased interior temperatures results in the syntheses of successively heavier elements. Then, eventually, after losing part of its mass, the star will decline in its heat and radiation, until it ceases to be. Some stars will not end in darkness but rather in a burst of galactic brilliance, as supernovae. The products of their nucleosynthesis broadcast into space then may contribute to the substance of second- or even third-generation stars.

Not as well documented yet as the stars, planetary evolution has been nevertheless elucidated by insights gained from stellar development. Newton's theory of gravitation first made it possible to approach planetary cosmogony from a scientific point of view. Kant, and independently some years later Laplace, built their nebular hypothesis (which still underlies present planetary theories) on the Newtonian groundwork. This hypothesis proposes that the sun had its origin in a rotating gas cloud. On contracting, equatorial sections of the cloud's outer layer were successively pulled away by centrifugal force. When these portions condensed, each of them gave rise to a new planet which continued to orbit in the same direction as the cloud of origin. The nebular hypothesis has come under repeated attack from the start, primarily because the sun would be expected to maintain the same momentum as its planets, while actually it moves much slower. Other ideas, including Sir James Jeans' near-collision hypothesis, were advanced and abandoned, and in 1944 the German astronomer Weizsäcker re-introduced the classical theory in a modernized version. He sees the original dust cloud as a system of vortices rather than a single rotating mass. At the boundaries, between groups of vortices, the particles condensed to form the planetesimals which later became the planets. Alfvén substituted the Newtonian mechanics on which the Kant-Laplace theory was based with a new branch of physics—magnetohydrodynamics. In applying this to astronomy, he was able to account for the braking of the initial solar rotation through transfer of the angular momentum to the interstellar medium along magnetic lines of force. Thus, the nebular hypothesis, with modifications, has now come to be widely accepted, and it would seem likely that as long as planetary evolution is indeed a part of stellar evolution, planetary systems should abound in the universe.

This is an important factor in the problem of life in the universe. We can only extrapolate what we have learned from our terrestrial experience, and earth, after all, is a planet. Therefore, we must assume that conditions not too dissimilar to the ones on earth would favor the origin of life anywhere in the universe. There are probably about 10^{20} stars. At least 10^{18} may gather planets around them. But what kind of solar system would be best suited to support a life-bearing planet? It would seem that a single star of a mass about equal to our sun could offer the duration of stable luminosity necessary for the unfolding of the biological time scale, and assure an approximately circular orbit for its planets. The prevalence of liquid water, which is essential for molecular interactions, would depend on the planet's distance from the star. A nonpoisonous atmosphere should be *sine qua non* for existing life.

Going down the line, assuming one out of a hundred stars to meet in succession each of the restrictive conditions, Shapley[3] arrives at the rather conservative estimate of at least 10^{10} earthlike planets in the universe, capable of supporting some kind of life. And, with the inexorable drive of evolution, it would stand to reason that there should even be numerous instances of intelligent life. Our solar system so far seems to have yielded only one habitat for evolved life. The conditions on Mars are thought to be fit for only the most lowly organized forms, if any at all; yet the peculiar orbital behavior of one of its moons, Phobos, has given rise to a tantalizing hypothesis which implicates not only highly evolved Martian life, but superior intelligence. In short, the Russian astrophysicist Shklovskii examined all the scientific considerations which would explain why Phobos is drawn toward Mars, probably to crash there in about 10–20 million years. None of the explanations fit quite as well as the supposition that this is not a natural, solid celestial body, but a hollowed-out sphere; in fact, an artificial satellite. Put into orbit long, long ago, at the heyday of a civilization since extinct, Phobos (and possibly Deimos, the second moon) remains the only witness to its existence. This is perhaps more imaginative than a future close-up view could substantiate, but it surely emphasizes the fascinating aspects of space exploration.

Venus has regained its place on the list of candidates for life-bearing planets. The idea that extremely hot, life-forbidding temperatures prevail there had been based on thermal emissions in the microwave spectrum; they now are thought to be radio emissions resulting from rapid-fire electric discharges in the Venusian atmosphere.[4] However, this would also require an on-the-spot confirmation.

Although we have just barely begun to explore our own solar system, we already realize that it might be more profitable to search other star systems for intelligent life. The nearest single stars of appropriate mass are Epsilon Eridani and Tau Ceti. Only 11 light-years away, they are close enough to rub elbows with by cosmic standards, but the actual getting-in-touch with our would-be space neighbors presents a problem of truly astronomic proportions by earth standards. Even if technically feasible, a round trip there and back would far exceed the life span of terrestrial expedition members. A radio exchange at the speed of light, though more practicable, would still be rather tedious with 22 years between questions and answers. The American radio astronomer Frank Drake, convinced that contact with extraterrestrials is not only possible but probable, developed in 1960 a 27 meter radio antenna at Green Banks, W. Va., in order to scan the space around those two stars for radio signals of 21 centimeter wavelength. This should be recognizable to all astronomers, anywhere in space, as the wavelength of hydrogen emission, and is also at minimum cosmic noise. Though well conceived, this preliminary Project Ozma folded in 1961. Most astronomers who are of a like mind with Drake now believe that the highly technical civilizations which would be able to reach us with their radio beacons are on much more distant planets, possibly farther than 100 light-years from earth.

Now, instead of just "sitting by the telephone" and waiting for signals directed at us, we could try to "eavesdrop" as it were, on any interplanetary communications beamed to someone else. This course does not solve the problem, however, but rather compounds it. The often painful language barrier existing even among us terrestrials gives an indication of what we may look forward to in case of an intercepted message from outer space. Once again the saying that one picture is worth a thousand words finds affirmation. Drake has coded a hypothetical extraplanetary communication in 551 binary units which, correctly translated, conveys in pictorial form an astonishing amount of information of universal meaning. The Dutch mathematician Freudenthal recently devised a non-graphic, wordless language called Lincos, which manages to express abstract concepts. Combined with the pictorial method, this could present a way to make the entire intellectual content of whole civilizations available in a relatively short time. Laser beams have also been considered as optical communication bridges across the vast distances between inhabited planets.

But all this has not brought us face to face with our extra-terrestrial neighbors, reported encounters with "passengers" of so-called UFO's notwithstanding. If and when we finally meet, will we experience instant recognition, horror, or embarrassment? In anticipation, this question has been answered in different ways. At one extreme is Simpson's[5] thesis that evolution, based on chance events, with natural selection operating under given conditions, would result in one of any number of biologies, which conceivably could be quite different under different conditions. It would be quite unreasonable, according to his view, to expect any-where else even an approximation of the events which led to the development of mankind on earth. The opposite view holds that, far from being the outcome of a fortuitous coming-together of chemicals and conditions, the course of organic evolution leads inevitably from hydrogen to humi-noids. That there will be certain relatively minor differences cannot be doubted if we consider the variability of our own species. But, as Bieri[6] points out in his cogently developed argument, conceptualizing beings in outer space won't be spheres, pyramids, cubes, or pancakes. Neither will they sport green skin, antenna systems, or other fanciful at-tributes. "In all probability they will look an awful lot like us."

References

1. H. Alfvén, "Worlds—Antiworlds," W. H. Freeman & Com-pany, San Francisco, 1966.
2. _____, *Sci. Am.* **216,** 106 (April, 1967).
3. H. Shapley, "View from a Distant Star," Basic Books, Incor-porated, New York, 1963.

4. D. C. Applebaum, P. Harteck, R. R. Reeves, Jr., and B. A. Thompson, *J. Geophys. Res.* **71,** 5541 (1966).
5. G. G. Simpson, *Science* **143,** 796 (1964).
6. R. Bieri, *Amer. Scientist* **52**, 452 (1964).

Supplementary Readings

Asimov, I., "Asimov's Biographical Encyclopedia of Science and Technology," Doubleday & Co., Inc., Garden City, N.Y., 1964. For helpful information on the people who contributed to the emerging picture of the universe.

Gatland, K. W., Dempster, D. D., "The Inhabited Universe," A Premier Book, Fawcett World Library, N.Y., 1963.

Shklovskii, I. S., and Sagan, C., "Intelligent Life in the Universe," Holden-Day, Inc., San Francisco, 1966. This book offers a wealth of information in a highly readable form; an enjoyable adventure for even moderately intelligent terrestrials.

Singer, C., "A Short History of Scientific Ideas to 1900," Oxford Paperbacks, 1962. For background to Aristotelian and Ptolemaic world systems see particularly pp. 54, 90.

Sullivan, W., "We Are Not Alone," McGraw-Hill Book Co., N.Y., 1964.

Wagoner, R. V., "Cosmological Element Production," *Science 155*, 1369 (1967).

Meadow, A. J., "Stellar Evolution," Pergamon Press, N. Y., 1967.

Index